REVISE KEY STAGE 3
Mathematics
STUDY WORKBOOK
Higher

Series Consultant: Harry Smith

Authors: Bobbie Johns and Sharon Bolger

Our study resources are the smart choice for those studying Key Stage 3 Mathematics, and preparing to start the GCSE (9-1) Mathematics Higher Course. This Study Workbook will help you to:

- **Organise** your study with the one-topic-per-page format
- **Simplify** your study by writing straight into the book
- **Track** your progress with at-a-glance check boxes
- **Improve** your understanding with guided questions to build confidence, and hints to support key study points
- **Develop** your technique with practice questions and full answers
- **Progress** towards the GCSE (9-1) Maths Higher course with problem solving practice.

Check out the Key Stage 3 Study Guide too!

Make sure that you have practised every topic covered in this book, with the accompanying Key Stage 3 Mathematics Study Guide. It gives you:

- A 1-to-1 page match with this Study Workbook
- Explanations of key concepts delivered in short memorable chunks
- Key hints and tips to reinforce your learning
- Worked examples showing you how to lay out your answers.

For the full range of Pearson revision titles across KS2, KS3, GCSE, Functional Skills, AS/A Level and BTEC visit: www.pearsonschools.co.uk/revise

Contents

Multiplication and division

1 Work out using known facts or doubling and halving.

(a) 52 × 4

= 50 × 4 + 2 × 4

= .... + ...

= ....

(b) 25 × 32

= 50 × 16

= 100 × ....8........

= ....

(c) 45 × 6

= .... × ....

= ....

(d) 0.3 × 0.7

= 3 × 7 ÷ 100

= .... ÷ 100

= ....

(e) 320 ÷ 80

= 32 ÷ ....

= ....

(f) 400 ÷ 25

= 800 ÷ 50

= .... ÷ ....

= ....

2 Work out

(a) 273 × 16

```
      2 7 3
×       1 6
...................   (273 × 6)
............0 + (273 × 10)
...................
```

(b) 315 × 28

```
      3 1 5
×       2 8
...................
...................
...................
```

(c) 407 × 34

....

3 A tray holds 36 apples. How many apples could 125 trays hold?

.... apples

4 Work out each of the following, giving any remainder as a decimal.

Use dot notation for the recurring decimal.

(a) 875 ÷ 5

```
     1.........
5)8³7 5
```

875 ÷ 5 = ...

(b) 652 ÷ 4

```
    ........
4)6 5 2
```

....

(c) 296 ÷ 5

....

(d) 399 ÷ 8

....

(e) 328 ÷ 6

....

5 Work out

(a) 6528 ÷ 17

Write out some multiples of the divisor. Then divide in the normal way.

Multiples of 17: 17, 34, ...

....

17)6 5 2 8   6528 ÷ 17 = ...

(b) 12 466 ÷ 23

....

Decimals

 1 Round 3.82745 to

> To round to the nearest whole number, look at the digit in the tenths place. It is 5 or more, so round **up**.

   (a) the nearest whole number   (b) 1 decimal place (1 d.p.)   (c) 2 decimal places (2 d.p.)

....

 2 Round each number to 1 significant figure (s.f.).

> Round to the first non-zero digit.

   (a) 6289   (b) 76.5   (c) 0.8746

   6000   ....

 3 Round each number to 2 significant figures.

> In (a), the second significant figure is the 7, so look at the next digit to decide whether to round up or down.

   (a) 3765   (b) 0.3687   (c) 0.00936

   3..............................   ....

 4 Round these numbers to the number of significant figures shown.

> Initial or 'leading' zeros do not count as significant figures.

   (a) 27 465 (3 s.f.)   (b) 2 847 915 (1 s.f.)   (c) 0.003 749 96 (4 s.f.)

....

  5 Work out an estimate for

   (a) 5.8×4.3 (b) $\dfrac{7.19 \times 37.81}{82.7 \div 19.3}$

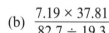
> Round each number to 1 s.f.

....

 6 Sue can make a shirt from 2.95 m of fabric.
Approximately how many shirts can Sue make from 32.98 m of fabric?

> Round to 1 or 2 s.f.

.... shirts

Using powers of 10

1 Complete the table to write these populations as whole numbers and as millions.

Country	Population	Population
Albania	2 892 000	.... million
Costa Rica	....	4.87 million
Barbados	285 000	.... million
Brunei	....	0.430 million

> To divide by 1 000 000 move the digits 6 places to the right.
> To multiply by 1 000 000 move the digits 6 places to the left.

2 (a) A mansion is for sale for £3.25 million. Write this as a whole number.

£.............................

(b) The population of Cheltenham was 115 700 in the 2011 census. Write this as a decimal number of millions.

.... million

3 Work out

(a) 39.58×10^2

= 39.58 × 100

= ....

(b) $9376 \div 10^3$

= 9376 ÷ 1000

= ....

> Write powers of 10 as whole numbers before multiplying or dividing.

(c) 3.8×10^4

= .... × ....

= ....

(d) $52 \div 10^2$

....

....

(e) 725×10^{-3}

....

....

(f) $47.9 \div 10^{-2}$

....

....

> Remember these equivalences for negative powers:
> $\times 10^{-1} = \times 0.1 = \div 10$
> $\times 10^{-2} = \times 0.01 = \div 100$
> $\div 10^{-1} = \div 0.1 = \times 10$
> $\div 10^{-2} = \div 0.01 = \times 100$

(g) 83.27×10^{-2}

....

....

(h) $514.87 \div 10^{-3}$

....

....

4 Work out

(a) 49×0.1

= 49 ÷ 10

= ....

(b) 62×0.01

= 62 ÷ 100

= ....

(c) $51 \div 0.1$

....

....

(d) 79×0.01

....

....

5 Write the equivalent multiplication calculation for dividing by 0.001.

....

Calculating with decimals

1 Work out

> First, estimate by rounding each number to 1 s.f. Ignore the decimal point and work out the multiplications as whole numbers. Then put the same number of decimal places in the answer as are in the question.

(a) 45.28 × 18

Estimate: 50 × 20 = ...

```
    4 5 2 8
×       1 8
_____

_____
```

(b) 3.6 × 4.8

Estimate: ....

....

(c) 2.7 × 3.9

....

....

2 Work out

> To divide by a decimal you multiply both parts of the division by the same power of 10 so the divisor is a whole number. Then write out the first few multiples of the divisor to help with the division.

(a) 42.65 ÷ 5

```
      8 . ...........
5)4⁴2².6 5
```

42.65 ÷ 5 = ...

(b) 78.68 ÷ 1.4

....

(c) 108.72 ÷ 2.4

....

3 Share a bill for £277.60 equally between 16 people. How much does each person pay?

> Write out the multiples of 16 first.

£.............................

4 A regular hexagon has a perimeter of 74.4 cm.
What is the length of one of its sides?

> The perimeter is the total distance around the shape. A regular hexagon has six sides of equal length.

.............................cm

5 How many complete 1.5 kg bags of potatoes can be filled from a 20 kg sack of potatoes?

.... bags

6 Marta says that 32.6 × 17.4 = 5672.4. Show or explain why she is **not** correct.

....

4

Negative numbers

1 Work out

(a) $3 - 6$

....

(b) $1 + (-5)$

$= 1 - 5$

$= $ ....

(c) $-2 - 4$

....

(d) $8 - (-2)$

....

Guided

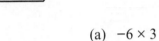

2 Work out

> When multiplying or dividing one number by another:
> • if the signs are different, the answer is negative
> • if the signs are the same, the answer is positive.

(a) -6×3

....

(b) -5×-7

....

(c) $2 \times -9 \times -5$

$= -18 \times$ ....

$=$ ....

(d) $12 \div -2$

....

(e) $-24 \div -8$

....

(f) $-100 \div -25 \times -2$

....

(g) $(-6)^2$

....

(h) $(-1)^3$

....

3 Between 6 pm and 2 am the next day, the temperature fell 9 degrees. At 2 am it was $-2\,°C$. What was the temperature at 6 pm?

You will need to use problem-solving skills throughout your exam – **be prepared!**

............................°C

4 The table shows information about the average maximum temperature in different cities in December.

City	Reykjavík	Cape Town	London	Moscow
Temperature	$-4\,°C$	$24\,°C$	$7\,°C$	$-8\,°C$

Work out

(a) the difference between the temperature in London and the temperature in Moscow

.... degrees

(b) the difference between the temperature in Cape Town and the temperature in Reykjavík.

.... degrees

(c) The average temperature in New York is 11 degrees higher than in Reykjavík in December. What is the average December temperature in New York?

............................°C

5
2	−2	−8	5	−3	4

> Try different combinations of numbers. The smallest possible product will be negative.

(a) Choose two numbers from the box to make the smallest possible product.

You will need to use problem-solving skills throughout your exam – **be prepared!**

....

(b) Choose three numbers from the box to make the greatest possible product.

....

Place-value calculations

1 Write the names of the competitors in finishing order, starting with the winner.

> For each event, think about whether the winner takes the most/least time or has the longest/shortest jump.

(a)

400 m	Time (seconds)
Ellie	52.75
Fiona	52.9
Gina	52.699
Hetty	52.745

(b)

Long jump	Distance (metres)
Aaron	3.4
Brendan	3.409
Caleb	3.38
Darius	3.42

....

....

....

....

2 Order these decimals from highest to lowest.

−9.4, −9.399, −9.44, −9.38

.... , ... , ... , ...

3 Use the fact that $0.72 \times 3.5 = 2.52$ to work out

> Compare the number of decimal places in the multiplication fact with the number of decimal places in each calculation.

> Rearranging the multiplication fact gives $2.52 \div 3.5 = 0.72$

(a) 72×3.5

$= 2.52 \times 100$

$= ....$

(b) 0.072×35

$= 2.52 \div 10 \times ....$

$= ....$

(c) $252 \div 3.5$

....

....

(d) $25.2 \div 7.2$

....

....

4 Use the fact that $48 \times 96 = 4608$ to work out

(a) 24×96

....

....

(b) 48×192

....

....

(c) $460.8 \div 0.48$

....

....

(d) $4.608 \div 9.6$

....

....

5 Tess says that $54.32 \div 9.7 = 0.56$. Show or explain why Tess is **not** correct.

....

6

Complex operations

1 Work out the operations needed to make each answer correct.

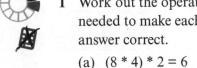
> Try out some combinations until you get the correct answer. Remember the priority of operations and do the operation inside the brackets first.

(a) $(8 * 4) * 2 = 6$

(b) $(8 * 4) * 2 = 8$

....

2 Show that $(9 - 4)^2 \neq 9^2 - 4^2$

3 Work out each of the following and then check with your calculator.

> Always work out the values in brackets first, remembering the order of operations. Simplify any fraction.

Guided

(a) $6 \times (\sqrt{144} - 3^2)$

$= 6 \times (12 - 9)$

$.......... \times .... = ...$

(b) $9^2 - (4 \times \sqrt{64})$

$= .... - (4 \times ....)$

$= .... - .... = ...$

(c) $(4^2 - \sqrt{121})^2$

$= (.......... - ....)^2$

$= ....^2 = ...$

(d) $\sqrt[3]{4 \times 4^2}$

$= \sqrt[3]{..........} \times \sqrt{..........}$

$= \sqrt[3]{..........}$

$= \sqrt{..........}$

(e) $\sqrt{6^2 + 8^2}$

$= \sqrt{..........} + \sqrt{..........}$

$= \sqrt{..........}$

$= \sqrt{..........}$

(f) $\dfrac{30 \times 2^3}{\sqrt[3]{5^2} \times \sqrt{100} \div 2}$

$= \dfrac{.......... \times ....}{\sqrt[3]{..........} \times .... \div ....}$

$= \dfrac{..........}{\sqrt[3]{..........}} = \dfrac{..........}{..........}$

$= ....$

4 Use a calculator to work out $\dfrac{15^2 - \sqrt{169}}{1.8^2}$

Write your answer correct to 2 decimal places.

....

5 Work out

(a) $\sqrt{13} \times \sqrt{13}$

(b) $\sqrt{99} \times \sqrt{99}$

....

6 Given that $49 \times 81 = 3969$, work out $\sqrt{3969}$

$\sqrt{3969} = \sqrt{49 \times 81} = \sqrt{49} \times \sqrt{..........} = ... \times ....$

$= ....$

> You will need brilliant problem-solving skills to succeed in GCSE – **get practising now!**

PROBLEM SOLVED!

7 Given that $64 \times 215 = 8000$, work out $\sqrt[3]{8000}$

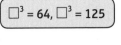
> $\Box^3 = 64, \Box^3 = 125$

....

PROBLEM SOLVED!

Upper and lower bounds

1 The length of a phone is given as 15 cm to the nearest centimetre.

(a) What is its smallest possible length?

●————○
14.5   15   15.5 cm

..............................cm

(b) What is its greatest possible length?

..............................cm

2 Give the upper and lower bounds for each measurement.
Write your answer as an inequality.

(a) A width, w, of 9 cm to the nearest centimetre.

...............cm ⩽ w < ....cm

(b) A mass, m, of 6 kg to the nearest kilogram.

.... ⩽ m < ....

(c) A capacity, c, of 750 ml to the nearest 50 ml.

....

(d) A length, l, of 150 cm to the nearest 10 cm.

....

(e) A capacity, c, of 2 litres to the nearest 100 ml.

....

| In part (c), the nearest unit is 50 ml, so half of this is 25 ml. | The actual measurement could be half a unit more or less than the rounded figure. |

3 The capacity of a car fuel tank is 64 litres. It has a 5% error interval. Work out the maximum and minimum capacities of the tank.

| Work out 5% of 64 litres. Add this to find the maximum capacity, and subtract it to find the minimum capacity. |

Maximum capacity: ....litres

Minimum capacity: ....litres

4 The width of a field is 14 m to the nearest metre.
The length of the field is 18 m to the nearest metre.

(a) Work out the maximum possible area of the field.

Upper bound × upper bound = ... × .... = ... m²

(b) Work out the minimum possible perimeter of the field.

| Use the lower bound of both measurements. |

.... metres

Powers

Guided

1 Write each product as a single power.

> To **multiply** powers of the same number, **add** the powers.
> To **divide** powers of the same number, **subtract** the powers.
> When **raising** a power to another power, **multiply** the powers.

(a) $7^2 \times 7^4 = 7^{2+4} =$ ....

(b) $6^9 \div 6^4 = 6^{\cdots - \cdots} =$ ....

(c) $10^3 \times 10 =$ ....

(d) $11^5 \div 11 =$ ....

(e) $(5^4)^3 = 5^{4 \times 3} =$ ....

(f) $(10^6)^5 =$ ....

(g) $3^5 \times 3^4 \div 3 = 3^{5+4-1} =$ ....

(h) $5^6 \times 5 \div 5^5 =$ ....

$=$ ....

2 Simplify $\dfrac{7^5 \times 7^3}{7^2 \times 7^4}$

> First, simplify the top and bottom of the fraction separately.

....

3 Write 3^{-4} as a fraction.

> A negative power is the reciprocal of a positive power.

....

4 Work out

(a) $\left(\dfrac{1}{7}\right)^2$

....

(b) 4^{-3}

....

(c) $(-3)^3$

....

(d) $(-8)^2$

....

(e) $\left(\dfrac{3}{10}\right)^2$

....

(f) 15^1

....

(g) 20^0

....

(h) $36^{\frac{1}{2}}$

....

(i) $1000^{\frac{1}{3}}$

....

Had a go ☐   Nearly there ☐   Nailed it! ☐

Standard form

1 Write each product as an ordinary number.

> **Guided**

(a) 3.2×10^3

$= 3.2 \times 1000$

$= \dotsc$

(b) 4.8×10^5

$\dotsc$

> Multiplying by a negative power is the same as dividing by a positive power.

(c) 6.25×10^3

$\dotsc$

(d) 7.091×10^4

$\dotsc$

(e) 5.8×10^{-3}

$= 5.8 \div 10^3$

$= 5.8 \div 1000$

$= \dotsc$

(f) 3.45×10^{-2}

$\dotsc$

(g) 2.094×10^{-1}

$\dotsc$

2 Write each number in standard form.

> **Guided**

> Numbers $\geqslant 1$ have a positive power when in standard form.

(a) 7000

$= \dotsc \times 10^{\dotsc}$

(b) 5200

$= \dotsc \times 10^{\dotsc}$

(c) 867 000

$= \dotsc \times \dotsc$

3 Write each number in standard form.

> **Guided**

> Numbers < 1 have a negative power when in standard form.

(a) 0.123

$= \dotsc \times 10^{-1}$

(b) 0.0029

$= \dotsc \times 10^{-\dotsc}$

(c) 0.09

$= \dotsc \times \dotsc$

4 Write each number in standard form.

(a) 25

$\dotsc$

(b) 0.36

$\dotsc$

(c) 0.0045

$\dotsc$

(d) 386

$\dotsc$

(e) 0.030 06

$\dotsc$

(f) 68 000

$\dotsc$

5 Work out each of the following, giving your answers in standard form.

> When adding or subtracting numbers in standard form, write them out as ordinary numbers first. Then add or subtract, before rewriting the final answer in standard form, if required.

(a) $\dfrac{1.2 \times 10^6}{4 \times 10^3}$

(b) $9.8 \times 10^2 + 3.5 \times 10^4$

(c) $7 \times 10^5 \times 6 \times 10^{-3}$

$\dotsc$

$\dotsc$

$\dotsc$

6 The diameter of Mars is 6800 km and the diameter of Jupiter is 142 800 km. Work out the difference between their diameters. Give your answer in standard form.

$\dotsc$ km

Calculator buttons

1 Match each calculator button to its function.

A $x^\square$ (i) Input a proper fraction

B ⬚√⬚   (ii) Input a number in standard form

C ³√⬚   (iii) Cube the number entered

D 🔲   (iv) Input a mixed number

E x^3 (v) Take a root > 2 of the number entered

F $x10^x$ (vi) Use index key for powers > 2

G 🔳   (vii) Take cube root of the number entered

2 Use your calculator to work out each of the following.

(a) (i) 7^4 .... (ii) 3^{-5} ....

(iii) $\sqrt[3]{12\,167}$ .... (iv) $\sqrt[5]{1024}$ ....

(b) (i) 4.098×10^7 ....

(ii) $3.157 \times 10^{-3} \times 2.75 \times 10^4$ ....

3 Find the value of $\sqrt[3]{174}$ correct to 3 decimal places. ....

4 Use the 🔳 button on your calculator to change each mixed number to an improper fraction.

> Use the arrow keys when entering the mixed number.

(a) $2\frac{5}{6}$ .... (b) $4\frac{8}{9}$ ....

5 Use the 🔲 button on your calculator to change each improper fraction to a mixed number.

> Enter the fraction, then press =, SHIFT (second function) and the S⇔D button.

(a) $\frac{17}{3}$ .... (b) $\frac{21}{5}$ .... (c) $\frac{35}{9}$ ....

6 Use the 🔲 and 🔳 buttons on your calculator to work out each of the following. Give your answers as mixed numbers.

(a) $\frac{2}{3}+\frac{4}{5}$ (b) $4\frac{5}{6}-2\frac{1}{5}$ (c) $\frac{4}{5}\div\frac{3}{20}$ (d) $4\frac{2}{3}\times 2\frac{3}{5}$

....

7 A grain of salt has a mass of approximately 6.5×10^{-5} kg. How many grains of salt are in a 2 kg bag of salt? Give your answer to 2 significant figures.

> You will need brilliant problem-solving skills to succeed in GCSE – **get practising now!**

.... grains

Prime factors

1 Draw a prime factor tree for each number. Write each number as a product of its prime factors.

(a)   80

②   40

②   ......

②   ......

...   ...

80 = 2 × 2 × 2 × .... × ....

(b)   150

....

150 = ...

2 Write each number as a product of its prime factors. Give your answer using index notation.

> Draw a factor tree for each number. Circle the prime factors.

(a) 245

(b) 320

245 = ...

320 = ...

3 Circle the numbers that are written as a product of their prime factors.

> Check that all the factors are prime numbers.

27 = 3 × 9   45 = 1 × 3 × 3 × 5   72 = 2 × 2 × 2 × 3 × 3

4 $84 = 2^2 \times 3 \times 7$

(a) Write 168 as a product of its prime factors using index notation.

> $84 \times \square = 168$

....

(b) Write 84^2 as a product of its prime factors using index notation.

....

HCF and LCM

1 (a) Draw factor trees for 32 and 56 and write their prime factor decompositions.

        32   56

      32 = ...   56 = ...

(b) Use the prime factor decompositions to work out the highest common factor (HCF) and lowest common multiple (LCM) of 32 and 56.

    HCF of 32 and 56 = ...

    LCM of 32 and 56 = ...

> For the HCF, write out each product without index notation. Underline the common factors in each list. Write these common factors as a product and work out the answer. To find the LCM, multiply the HCF by any remaining factors in both lists.

2 $72 = 2^3 \times 3^2$ and $48 = 2^4 \times 3$

Work out

(a) the HCF of 72 and 48   (b) the LCM of 72 and 48

> Write each product without index notation.

....

3 A teacher wants to provide each of his 32 students with a pencil and a pen. Pencils come in packs of 12 and pens come in packs of 8. He wants to buy the same number of pens as pencils. What are the smallest numbers of packs of pencils and pens he can buy so that there is a pen and a pencil for each student?

> Work out the LCM. Is this enough? What is the next common multiple? How many of each pack will he need to buy?

> You will need brilliant problem-solving skills to succeed in GCSE – **get practising now!**

.... packs of pencils   .... packs of pens

4 A haberdasher has two pieces of ribbon, which are 42 m and 70 m in length. She wants to cut them into smaller pieces of equal length. What is the longest length she can cut them into?

> Do you need to work out the LCM or the HCF?

.... metres

Fractions and percentages

1 Work out

> Divide by the denominator and multiply by the numerator.

(a) $\frac{2}{3}$ of 480 = 480 ÷ 3 × 2 = £ ....

(b) $\frac{4}{5}$ of £2500 ....

2 Work out

> Work out 10% first and use this to find other percentages.

(a) 15% of £750   10% = 750 ÷ 10 = 75, 5% = 75 ÷ 2 = 37.5, 15% = ...

(b) 35% of 4200 m*l*   ....m*l*

(c) 80% of 3 metres   .... metres

3 Use a calculator to work out each of the following to the nearest penny.

(a) $\frac{5}{13}$ of £208

(b) $\frac{11}{24}$ of £5498

£............................

£............................

4 Use your preferred calculator method to work out each of the following to the nearest penny.

> You can either convert the percentage to a decimal multiplier, or you can divide the amount by 100 then multiply by the percentage.

(a) 47% of £850

(b) 23% of £720

(c) 6.5% of £95

£............................

£............................

£............................

5 Which is more, 45.6% of £2450 or $\frac{7}{15}$ of £2540? You must show all your working.

....

6 Concrete is made by mixing cement, sand and gravel. 12% of the mixture is cement, $\frac{21}{40}$ is sand and the rest is gravel. Mick makes 25 kg of concrete.

(a) Work out the quantity of each material, including the gravel.

........................kg cement   ....kg sand   ....kg gravel

(b) What percentage of the concrete is gravel?

........................%

7 Write these amounts in order of size. Start with the largest amount.

$\frac{14}{17}$ of £3500   72% of £3800   57.5% of £5100 $\frac{13}{19}$ of £4200

....

Equivalence

Guided

1 Convert the decimals to percentages and the percentages to decimals.

(a) 0.65

(b) 0.2

(c) 0.08

= 0.65 × 100 = ...%

..........%

..........%

(d) 34%

(e) 250%

(f) 1.05

= 0...............

....

..........%

> ×100
>
> Decimal   Percentage
>
> ÷100

Guided

2 Convert the decimals and percentages into fractions or mixed numbers. Write your answer in its simplest form.

> Write the decimal or percentage as a fraction out of 100 and then simplify.

(a) 0.24

$= \dfrac{24}{100} = \dfrac{........}{........}$

(b) 35%

$= \dfrac{........}{........} = \dfrac{........}{........}$

(c) 0.6

$= \dfrac{60}{100} = \dfrac{........}{........}$

(d) 0.09

$= \dfrac{........}{........}$

(e) 8%

$= \dfrac{........}{........} = \dfrac{........}{........}$

(f) 1.03

$= \dfrac{........}{........} = ...\dfrac{........}{........}$

(g) 115%

$= \dfrac{........}{........} = ...\dfrac{........}{........}$

Guided

3 Write each fraction as a percentage and as a decimal.

> Simplify or use equivalence to write the fraction out of 10 or 100.

(a) $\dfrac{27}{50}$ $= \dfrac{........}{100} = ...\% \equiv 0. ....$

(b) $\dfrac{18}{24}$ $= \dfrac{........}{4} \times \dfrac{25}{25} = \dfrac{........}{........} = ...\% \equiv 0. ....$

(c) $\dfrac{28}{40}$ ....

4 Maisie has a money-off coupon showing a percentage saving. She has saved 27p on a product priced at £1.35. What percentage saving was shown on the coupon?

..........................%

5 Matt scores 120 out of 150 in paper A and 127 out of 160 in paper B. In which paper does he achieve the higher percentage score? You must show all your working.

Paper ....

6 60 dogs are shown at a dog show. 36 are male. What percentage are **female**?

..........................%

15

Recurring decimals

1 Write each decimal using dot notation.

> Draw a dot over the first and last digits of a recurring group.

(a) 4.333 333…   (b) 2.186 666…   (c) 1.232 323 23…   (d) 5.456 456 456…

....

2 Use a calculator to convert each mixed number to a decimal.

(a) $1\frac{4}{9}$ (b) $4\frac{1}{3}$ (c) $5\frac{11}{12}$

> Keep the whole number the same; just convert the fraction part.

....

Guided

3 Change each fraction into a decimal using division.

> Write the fraction as a division: numerator ÷ denominator.

(a) $\frac{6}{11}$ (b) $\frac{8}{9}$ (c) $2\frac{1}{12}$

$$\begin{array}{r} 0.\,5\ 4\ 5\ 4 \\ 11\overline{)6.^{6}0^{5}0^{6}0^{5}0} \end{array}$$

$\frac{6}{11} = 0.5454 =$ ....

4 Write each fraction as a decimal.

(a) $\frac{1}{9}$ (b) $\frac{89}{99}$ (c) $\frac{701}{999}$

....

5 Match each fraction with its decimal equivalent.

> Use a calculator.

$\frac{7}{9}$ $\frac{5}{7}$ $\frac{2}{3}$ $\frac{7}{12}$ $\frac{7}{8}$ $\frac{8}{11}$

$0.\dot{6}$ $0.\dot{7}\dot{2}$ 0.875 $0.\dot{7}$ $0.\dot{7}14\,28\dot{5}$ $0.58\dot{3}$

6 Prove, using division, that

(a) $\frac{3}{7} = 0.\dot{4}2857\dot{1}$ (b) $3\frac{5}{12} = 3.41\dot{6}$

Guided

7 Write as fractions in their simplest form.

> Write the decimal in full and call it n. Multiply it by 10 (for 1 d.p.), 100 (for 2 d.p.) or 1000 (for 3 d.p.). Then subtract n to get rid of the decimal part.

(a) $0.\dot{2}$ (b) $0.\dot{2}\dot{7}$ (c) $0.\dot{4}5\dot{6}$

$n = 0.222\,222…$
$10n = 2.222\,222\,222…$
$10n - n = 9n = 2$

$n = \frac{.........}{.........}$ ....

Add and subtract fractions

Guided

1 Work out each of the following.
Write your answer in its simplest form.

> Find equivalent fractions with the same denominator. Add or subtract the numerators and then simplify the fraction if possible.

(a) $\frac{1}{4} + \frac{3}{5} = \frac{5}{20} + \frac{\cdots}{20} = \frac{\cdots}{\cdots}$

(b) $\frac{7}{12} - \frac{1}{3} = \frac{7}{12} - \frac{\cdots}{12} = \frac{\cdots}{\cdots} = \frac{\cdots}{\cdots}$

(c) $\frac{4}{5} - \frac{2}{3} = \frac{\cdots}{\cdots} - \frac{\cdots}{\cdots} = \frac{\cdots}{\cdots}$

Guided

2 Work out each of the following.
Write your answer in its simplest form.

> Add or subtract the whole numbers, and add or subtract the fraction parts separately, then combine. Change improper fractions to mixed numbers.

(a) $4\frac{1}{5} + 3\frac{3}{4} = (4 + 3) + \left(\frac{1}{5} + \frac{3}{4}\right) = 7 + \left(\frac{\cdots}{20} + \frac{\cdots}{20}\right) = \cdots \frac{\cdots}{\cdots}$

(b) $4\frac{5}{6} - 2\frac{2}{3} = (4 - 2) + \left(\frac{5}{6} - \frac{2}{3}\right) = \cdots + \left(\frac{\cdots}{\cdots} - \frac{\cdots}{\cdots}\right) = \cdots \frac{\cdots}{\cdots}$

(c) $3\frac{5}{9} - 1\frac{1}{6} = (\cdots) + \left(\frac{\cdots}{\cdots} - \frac{\cdots}{\cdots}\right)$

$= \cdots + \left(\frac{\cdots}{\cdots} - \frac{\cdots}{\cdots}\right)$

$= \cdots \frac{\cdots}{\cdots}$

Guided

3 Work out

(a) $4\frac{1}{3} - 2\frac{5}{6} = (4 - 2) + \left(\frac{1}{3} - \frac{5}{6}\right) = 2 + \left(\frac{2}{6} - \frac{5}{6}\right)$

> Work out the whole-number and fraction subtractions separately, then combine. Remember that adding a negative is the same as subtracting the positive.

$= 2 + \left(-\frac{3}{6}\right)$

$= 2 - \frac{1}{2} = \cdots \frac{\cdots}{\cdots}$

(b) $5\frac{3}{5} - 2\frac{5}{8}$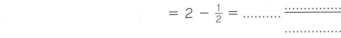

4 Oliver has $\frac{7}{8}$ of a block of chocolate. Luke has $\frac{5}{6}$ of the same size block of chocolate.
How much chocolate do they have in total?

.... blocks

PROBLEM SOLVED!

5 Mollie has completed $4\frac{1}{3}$ km of a charity walk.
Harry has completed $3\frac{4}{5}$ km of the same walk.
How much further has Mollie walked?

> You will need brilliant problem-solving skills to succeed in GCSE – **get practising now!**

.... km

Multiply and divide fractions

1 Work out each of the following.
Write your answer in its simplest form.

> Write any whole numbers as fractions with a denominator of 1. Multiply the numerators together and multiply the denominators together.
> If you cancel before multiplying, you don't need to simplify your answer at the end.

(a) $\frac{2}{5} \times 6$

$= \frac{2}{5} \times \frac{6}{1} = \frac{\ldots \times \ldots}{\ldots \times \ldots} = \frac{\ldots}{\ldots} = \ldots \frac{\ldots}{\ldots}$

(b) $\frac{6}{11} \times \frac{4}{9}$

$= \frac{\overset{2}{\cancel{6}}}{11} \times \frac{4}{\cancel{9}_3} = \frac{\ldots \times \ldots}{\ldots \times \ldots} = \frac{\ldots}{\ldots}$

(c) $\frac{3}{5} \times \frac{5}{9}$

$= \frac{\ldots \times \ldots}{\ldots \times \ldots} = \frac{\ldots}{\ldots}$

2 Work out

> Change ÷ to × and use the reciprocal of the second fraction (turn it upside down), then multiply as normal.

(a) $\frac{5}{6} \div \frac{1}{3}$

(b) $\frac{7}{8} \div \frac{1}{4}$

(c) $5 \div \frac{2}{3}$

$= \frac{5}{6} \times \frac{3}{1} = \ldots\ldots\ldots\ldots$

$\ldots\ldots\ldots\ldots\ldots\ldots\ldots\ldots\ldots$

$= \frac{5}{1} \times \frac{\ldots}{\ldots} = \ldots\ldots\ldots\ldots$

3 Work out

(a) $2\frac{3}{4} \div 4\frac{1}{8}$

> First change mixed numbers to improper fractions, then cancel before multiplying.

$= \frac{11}{4} \div \frac{33}{8} = \frac{\overset{1}{\cancel{11}}}{\cancel{4}_1} \times \frac{\overset{2}{\cancel{8}}}{\cancel{33}_3} = \frac{\ldots \times \ldots}{\ldots \times \ldots} = \frac{\ldots}{\ldots}$

(b) $3\frac{1}{3} \times 1\frac{4}{5}$ $\ldots\ldots\ldots\ldots\ldots\ldots\ldots\ldots\ldots\ldots$

(c) $2\frac{2}{3} \div 3\frac{5}{9}$ $\ldots\ldots\ldots\ldots\ldots\ldots\ldots\ldots\ldots\ldots$

$\ldots\ldots\ldots\ldots\ldots\ldots\ldots\ldots$

$\ldots\ldots\ldots\ldots\ldots\ldots\ldots\ldots$

4 Work out

(a) $\frac{7}{8} \times \frac{3}{4}$

(b) $\frac{3}{4} \div 6$

(c) $\frac{1}{6} \times \frac{4}{5}$

$\ldots\ldots\ldots\ldots\ldots\ldots$

$\ldots\ldots\ldots\ldots\ldots\ldots$

$\ldots\ldots\ldots\ldots\ldots\ldots$

(d) $\frac{3}{8} \div \frac{9}{16}$

(e) $3\frac{3}{5} \times 1\frac{3}{7}$

(f) $3\frac{3}{4} \div 2\frac{1}{12}$

$\ldots\ldots\ldots\ldots\ldots\ldots$

$\ldots\ldots\ldots\ldots\ldots\ldots$

$\ldots\ldots\ldots\ldots\ldots\ldots$

5 Amelie needs to cut a 10 m ball of twine into lengths of $1\frac{2}{3}$ m.
How many lengths of $1\frac{2}{3}$ m will she be able to cut?

$\ldots\ldots\ldots\ldots\ldots\ldots$ lengths

Surds

1 Circle the surds.

$\sqrt{10}$ $\sqrt{2}$ $\sqrt{16}$ $\sqrt{20.25}$ $\sqrt{25}$ $\sqrt{7}$

2 Simplify

> Don't leave an answer as a square root if it can be written as an integer.

Guided

(a) $\sqrt{9 \times 3}$

$= \sqrt{9} \times \sqrt{3}$

$= 3\sqrt{..........}$

(b) $\sqrt{5 \times 36}$

....

(c) $\sqrt{\dfrac{7}{64}}$

$= \dfrac{\sqrt{..........}}{\sqrt{..........}}$

$= \dfrac{..........}{..........}$

3 Simplify

> Look for factors that are square numbers.

Guided

(a) $\sqrt{63}$

$= \sqrt{9} \times \sqrt{..........}$

$= .... \times \sqrt{..........}$

$= .... \sqrt{..........}$

(b) $\sqrt{50}$

$= \sqrt{..........} \times \sqrt{..........}$

$= .... \times \sqrt{..........}$

$= .... \sqrt{..........}$

(c) $\sqrt{108}$

....

....

....

4 Write $\sqrt{20}$ in the form $k\sqrt{5}$ where k is an integer.

Guided

$\sqrt{20} = \sqrt{4 \times 5}$

$= \sqrt{4} \times \sqrt{5}$

$= .... \sqrt{..........}$

5 Write $\sqrt{98}$ in the form $k\sqrt{2}$ where k is an integer.

....

19

Number problem-solving

1 Here is part of Agata's gas bill.
How much does she have to pay, to the nearest penny?

> **Gas bill**
> Old reading   98 124 units
> New reading   99 032 units
> Cost per unit   5.76 pence

£ ....

PROBLEM SOLVED!

2 Three families split the cost of renting a holiday villa for two weeks. The cost of renting the villa is £1245 per week. The Browns pay 27% of the cost, the Greens pay $\frac{1}{3}$ of the cost and the Blacks pay the rest.

(a) How much does each family pay?

> You will need brilliant problem-solving skills to succeed in GCSE – **get practising now!**

Browns £ ....   Greens £ ....   Blacks £ ....

(b) What percentage of the total cost do the Blacks pay (to the nearest per cent)?

> The holiday rental is for two weeks.

.... %

PROBLEM SOLVED!

3 These are the prime factor decompositions of two numbers.

$M = 2^6 \times 3^4 \times 5^2 \times 7^2$ $N = 2^7 \times 5^3 \times 7^3 \times 11$

(a) Work out each number, giving your answers in standard form.

> You will need brilliant problem-solving skills to succeed in GCSE – **get practising now!**

$M = $ .... $N = $ ....

(b) Work out the HCF of M and N, giving your answer in index form and in standard form.

> To work out the HCF use the highest power for each common factor.

HCF = ... = ...

(c) Work out the LCM of M and N, giving your answer in standard form.

> The LCM is the HCF multiplied by any remaining factors not included in the HCF.

LCM = ...

4 The measurements of this rectangle are accurate to the nearest mm.

(a) Work out

(i) its smallest possible area   (ii) its largest possible area.

..........................cm²   ....cm²

(b) Write your answers to part (a) correct to 3 s.f.

(i) ....cm²   (ii) ....cm²

(c) Work out the difference between the largest possible perimeter and the smallest possible perimeter.

12.5cm

8.6cm

> Use lower and upper bounds.

..........................cm

Indices

1 Simplify

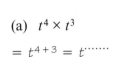

> Remember the rules for indices: $a^m \times a^n = a^{m+n}$ $a^m \div a^n = a^{m-n}$ $(a^m)^n = a^{mn}$
> Take care with negative and fractional indices.

(a) $t^4 \times t^3$

$= t^{4+3} = t^{\cdots\cdots}$

(b) $q^6 \div q^2$

$= q^{6-2} = \ldots\ldots\ldots$

(c) $(g^4)^3$

$= g^{4\times3} = \ldots\ldots\ldots$

(d) $a \times a^5 \div a^2$

....

(e) $b^{\frac{1}{2}} \times b^{\frac{1}{2}}$

$= b^{\frac{1}{2}+\frac{1}{2}} = b^{\cdots\cdots} = \ldots\ldots\ldots$

(f) $\dfrac{y^4 \times y}{y^3 \times y^3}$

$= \dfrac{\ldots\ldots}{\ldots\ldots} = \ldots\ldots\ldots$

2 Simplify fully

> Remember the rules for multiplying and dividing negative numbers.

(a) $2w^2 \times 4w^5$

$= 2 \times 4 \times w^2 \times w^5 = \ldots\ldots w^{\cdots\cdots}$

(b) $-5p \times 3p^3$

$= -5 \times 3 \times p \times p^3 = \ldots\ldots\ldots\ldots$

(c) $24h^5 \div 8h^3$

$= \dfrac{{}^{3}\cancel{24}h^5}{{}_{1}\cancel{8}h^3} = 3h^{5-3} = \ldots\ldots\ldots\ldots$

(d) $-30s^6 \div 10s$

....

3 Simplify fully

(a) $r^5 \times r$

....

(b) $(k^3)^{-2}$

....

(c) $t^{\frac{1}{3}} \times t^{\frac{1}{3}}$

....

(d) $6y^3 \times -2y^5$

....

(e) $32g^{\frac{1}{2}} \div -4g^{\frac{1}{2}}$

....

(f) $-40k^8 \div -5k^0$

....

4 Work out the value of y in each expression.

> Use the rules of indices to write an equation and solve for y.

(a) $a^y \times a^3 = a^7$

$y + 3 = 7$ so $y = \ldots\ldots$

(b) $d^9 \div d^y = d$

$9 - y = \ldots\ldots$ so $y = \ldots\ldots$

> You will need brilliant problem-solving skills to succeed in GCSE – **get practising now!**

(c) $(r^y)^4 = r^8$

....

(d) $(t^{-3})^y = t^{-9}$

....

(e) $e^{-y} = \dfrac{1}{e^5}$

....

(f) $y^{\frac{1}{2}} = 4$

....

(g) $y^{\frac{1}{3}} = 3$

....

Simplifying expressions

1 Simplify

> Only combine terms with exactly the same letter, letter combination or power. Each term includes the sign in front of it (+ or –). Numbers on their own are separate terms.

(a) $5x - 2y - 3x + 5y$

$= 5x - 3x - 2y + 5y = \ldots\ldots x + \ldots\ldots y$

(b) $9r - 7s + r + 10s$

$\ldots\ldots\ldots\ldots\ldots\ldots\ldots\ldots\ldots\ldots$

(c) $2p - 3q - 4p + q$

$\ldots\ldots\ldots\ldots\ldots\ldots\ldots\ldots\ldots$

(d) $-6t + 8u + t - 4u$

$\ldots\ldots\ldots\ldots\ldots\ldots\ldots\ldots\ldots$

(e) $10 - 5e + 2f - e - 6 - 5f$

$\ldots\ldots\ldots\ldots\ldots\ldots\ldots\ldots\ldots$

(f) $3a - 4a^2 - 2a + 2a^2$

$\ldots\ldots\ldots\ldots\ldots\ldots\ldots\ldots\ldots$

2 Simplify fully

> Multiply the numbers together and multiply the letters. Remember the rules for multiplying and dividing negative numbers and use the priority of operations.

(a) $3a \times 4b$

$= 3 \times 4 \times a \times b = \ldots\ldots\ldots\ldots$

(b) $-5g \times 3h$

$= -5 \times 3 \times g \times h = \ldots\ldots\ldots\ldots$

(c) $-6y \times -4y$

$\ldots\ldots\ldots\ldots\ldots\ldots\ldots\ldots\ldots$

3 Simplify fully

> Write the division as a fraction and cancel any common factors. Use the rules for dividing indices.

(a) $40a \div 5a$

$= \dfrac{{}^8\cancel{40}a}{{}_1\cancel{5}a} = 8a^{1-1} = 8a^{\ldots\ldots} = \ldots\ldots\ldots$

(b) $15g^3 \div 3g$

$= \dfrac{{}^5\cancel{15}g^3}{{}_1\cancel{3}g} = \ldots\ldots g^{\ldots\ldots}$

(c) $28b^5 \div 7b^3$

$\ldots\ldots\ldots\ldots\ldots\ldots\ldots\ldots\ldots$

4 Simplify fully

(a) $2a \times 3b \times 4c$

$\ldots\ldots\ldots\ldots\ldots\ldots\ldots\ldots$

(b) $-4k \times -5m \times -3k$

$\ldots\ldots\ldots\ldots\ldots\ldots\ldots\ldots$

(c) $-48r^3 \div -8r^5$

$\ldots\ldots\ldots\ldots\ldots\ldots\ldots\ldots$

(d) $8p \times 3q - 5p \times 2q$

$\ldots\ldots\ldots\ldots\ldots\ldots\ldots\ldots$

(e) $-36y^4 \div 4y$

$\ldots\ldots\ldots\ldots\ldots\ldots\ldots\ldots$

(f) $42a^2b \div 6ab^2$

$\ldots\ldots\ldots\ldots\ldots\ldots\ldots\ldots$

5 Write an expression for the perimeter of this rectangle. Give your answer in its simplest form.

$3x - 2y + 8$

$6x + y - 7$

$\ldots\ldots\ldots\ldots\ldots\ldots$

Expanding brackets

1 Expand the brackets.

Guided

(a) $5(4t - 2)$

$= 5 \times 4t + 5 \times -2$

$= \ldots\ldots\ldots\ldots - \ldots\ldots\ldots\ldots$

(b) $4f(3f - 5)$

$= 4f \times 3f - 4f \times 5$

$= \ldots\ldots\ldots\ldots - \ldots\ldots\ldots\ldots$

> Each term in the brackets is multiplied by the term outside the brackets. Take care when multiplying by a negative number.

(c) $-4m(3m - 2n)$

$= -4m \times \ldots\ldots\ldots\ldots + -4m \times \ldots\ldots\ldots\ldots$

$= \ldots\ldots\ldots\ldots + \ldots\ldots\ldots\ldots$

(d) $-a^2(3a + 4b)$

$= \ldots\ldots\ldots\ldots\ldots\ldots\ldots - \ldots\ldots\ldots\ldots\ldots\ldots\ldots$

$= \ldots\ldots\ldots\ldots\ldots\ldots\ldots\ldots\ldots$

(e) $2ab^2c(3bc - 5ac + 7ab^3)$

$= 2ab^2c \times \ldots\ldots\ldots\ldots + 2ab^2c \times \ldots\ldots\ldots\ldots + 2ab^2c \times \ldots\ldots\ldots\ldots$

$= \ldots\ldots\ldots\ldots\ldots\ldots\ldots\ldots\ldots\ldots\ldots\ldots\ldots\ldots\ldots\ldots$

2 Expand the brackets.

(a) $7r^2(2q - 5r)$

$\ldots\ldots\ldots\ldots\ldots\ldots\ldots\ldots\ldots\ldots$

(b) $-5b^3(4a^2 - 3b)$

$\ldots\ldots\ldots\ldots\ldots\ldots\ldots\ldots\ldots\ldots$

(c) $-4p^2q(3q^2 - 2p^3)$

$\ldots\ldots\ldots\ldots\ldots\ldots\ldots\ldots\ldots\ldots$

3 Expand and simplify

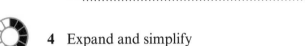

> Expand each set of brackets then simplify by collecting like terms.

Guided

(a) $3x(2y - 5x) + 2y(5x + 4y)$

$= 6xy - 15x^2 + 10xy + 8y^2$

$= \ldots\ldots\ldots\ldots\ldots\ldots\ldots\ldots\ldots\ldots\ldots\ldots\ldots\ldots\ldots\ldots$

(b) $6a(3b + 2a) - 3b(4a - 7b)$

$= 18ab + 12a^2 - \ldots\ldots\ldots\ldots ab + \ldots\ldots\ldots\ldots b^2$

$= \ldots\ldots\ldots\ldots\ldots\ldots\ldots\ldots\ldots\ldots\ldots\ldots\ldots\ldots$

4 Expand and simplify

(a) $4a^2b(5b - 3a) + 3ab^2(5a + 3b)$

(b) $7cd(4c - 2d) - 3cd(5c - 3d)$

$\ldots\ldots\ldots\ldots\ldots\ldots\ldots\ldots\ldots\ldots\ldots\ldots\ldots\ldots\ldots\ldots\ldots$

$\ldots\ldots\ldots\ldots\ldots\ldots\ldots\ldots\ldots\ldots\ldots\ldots\ldots\ldots\ldots\ldots\ldots$

5 Show that
$3x(2x - 5y) = -3x(5y - 2x)$

> Expand the brackets on each side of the equals sign separately and then simplify to show that they give the same terms.

Guided

LHS: $3x \times 2x + 3x \times -5y = \ldots\ldots\ldots\ldots\ldots\ldots\ldots$

RHS: $\ldots\ldots\ldots\ldots\ldots\ldots\ldots\ldots\ldots\ldots\ldots\ldots$

6 Write an expression for the area of the rectangle. Express your answer as the sum of two terms.

$5x + 3y$

$2x^2y$

$\ldots\ldots\ldots\ldots\ldots\ldots\ldots\ldots\ldots$

Expanding double brackets

1 Use the grid method to expand

> Take care when multiplying by a negative number.

(a) $(x + 4)(x - 3)$

	x	$+4$
x	x^2	....
-3	$-3x$	....

(b) $(x - 5)(x - 2)$

	x	-5
x	....	....
-2	....	....

$(x + 4)(x - 3) = x^2 - 3x + ... - ....$

$ = x^2 + ... - ....$

$(x - 5)(x - 2) = ...$

$ = ...$

2 Use the FOIL method to expand

> Simplify the two terms in x.

(a) $(x + 3)(x + 6)$

(b) $(x - 5)(x + 4)$

F   O   I   L

$x^2 + 6x + 3x + 18$

$(x + 3)(x + 6) = ...$

$...$

3 Use your preferred method to expand and simplify

> Write $(x - 6)^2$ as $(x - 6)(x - 6)$.

(a) $(x + 7)(x + 6)$

(b) $(x + 4)(x - 9)$

....

....

(c) $(x - 2)(x - 8)$

(d) $(x + 3)(x - 3)$

(e) $(x - 6)^2$

....

....

....

4 Expand and simplify

(a) $(3x - 5)(2x + 8)$

(b) $(4x - 3)(4x + 3)$

(c) $(5x + 6)^2$

....

....

....

5 Prove that $x^2 + b^2 \neq (x + b)^2$ (assuming $x \neq 0$ and $b \neq 0$).

> Expand the right-hand side to show that the terms on this side are different from the terms on the left-hand side.

....

6 Write an expression for the area of the rectangle. Express your answer as the sum of three terms.

$5x - 3$

$2x + 7$

....

Factorising

1 Factorise

> Look for the highest common factor of all the terms. In (a), the HCF of 24 and 16 is 8.

(a) $24a - 16b$ (b) $30y - 20$ (c) $3abc - 7bcd$

$= 8(3a - ....b)$ $= .... (............ - ....)$ $= .... (............ - ....)$

2 Factorise

> Look for the HCF. When you take the whole term out, replace it with 1.

(a) $3q^5 + 8q^3$ (b) $2e^7 + e^6$ (c) $6d^2 - 7d^4$

....

3 Factorise fully

> The HCF could be a combination of number and letter.

(a) $12ab - 8b$ (b) $30p^2q + 20pr$ (c) $35pqr - 25prs$

$= 4b (......... - ....)$ $= .... (......... + ...)$ $= .... (......... - ....)$

4 Factorise fully

(a) $15p^2q + 20pr$ (b) $18p^4 - 12p^2$ (c) $27x^5 + 36x^4$

....

5 Work out the missing terms to make these expansions true.

> $3 \times \square = 12$

(a) $\square a(3b - a) = 12 \square\square - \square a^{\square}$ (b) $15 \square^{\square} - 35\square h = \square g(\square\square - \square h)$

....

6 Factorise these quadratic expressions.

> When a quadratic expression is of the form $x^2 + bx + c$, look for pairs of numbers that add to give b and multiply to give c.

(a) $x^2 + 5x - 14$ (b) $x^2 + 11x + 24$ (c) $x^2 + 12x + 36$

....

7 The area of a rectangle is given by the quadratic expression $x^2 + x - 6$. One side is $x + p$ and the other side is $x - q$. Work out the value of p and the value of q.

> Factorise the quadratic expression.

....

More complex factorising

1 Draw lines to match each quadratic expression to its factorisation.

A $x^2 + 10x + 25$ B $9x^2 - 30x + 25$ C $x^2 - 25$ D $x^2 - 10x + 25$ E $9x^2 - 25$

(i) $(3x - 5)(3x - 5)$ (ii) $(x - 5)^2$ (iii) $(3x + 5)(3x - 5)$ (iv) $(x + 5)(x - 5)$ (v) $(x + 5)^2$

Guided

2 Factorise

> Look for a difference of two squares.

(a) $x^2 - 36$

$= (x + 6)(x - \text{.........})$

(b) $x^2 - 64$

$= (x + \text{.........})(x - \text{.........})$

(c) $x^2 - 144$

....

(d) $4x^2 - 16$

$= (2x + \text{.........})(\text{.........} - \text{.........})$

(e) $25x^2 - 49$

....

(f) $81x^2 - 100$

....

Guided

3 Use a difference of two squares to work out

(a) $47^2 - 43^2$

$= (47 + 43)(47 - 43)$

$= \text{.................} \times \text{.................}$

$= \text{.................................}$

(b) $85^2 - 45^2$

....

....

....

(c) $62^2 - 38^2$

....

....

....

4 Factorise

> When a quadratic expression is of the form $ax^2 + bx + c$, look for factor pairs of both a and c. Multiply factors of c by factors of a to find a combination that sums to b.

(a) $2x^2 - x - 15$

....

(b) $3x^2 + x - 14$

....

(c) $5x^2 + 17x + 6$

....

5 Show that $\dfrac{3x^2 + 13x + 12}{3x + 4} = x + 3$

> The denominator $(3x + 4)$ is likely to be part of the factorisation of $3x^2 + 13x + 12$.

6 The area of a rectangle is $(100x^2 - 64)$ cm². The rectangle has sides of length $(10x + a)$ cm and $(10x - a)$ cm. Write an expression for its perimeter in terms of x.

> Factorise the expression for the area to find the lengths of the sides first.

....

Substitution

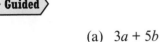

1 Work out the value of each expression when $a = 9$ and $b = 3$.

> Substitute the letters with their numerical value. Follow the priority of operations.

(a) $3a + 5b$

$= 3 \times 9 + 5 \times \dots\dots$

$= \dots\dots$

(b) $a^2 - b^2$

$= \dots\dots \times \dots\dots - \dots\dots \times \dots\dots$

$= \dots\dots$

(c) $\dfrac{a(b - 2)}{ab}$

....

....

(d) $3a(4b - 7)$

(e) $\dfrac{(a + b)^2}{(a - b)^2}$

(f) $b\sqrt{a}$

....

....

....

....

....

....

2 Work out the value of each expression.

(a) $5x^2$ when $x = 2$

....

(b) $3x^2 - 10y$ when $x = 5$ and $y = 3$

....

(c) $-6p^3$ when $p = -1$

....

(d) $\sqrt{q \times r - s}$ when $q = -9$, $r = -3$ and $s = 2$

....

(e) $\dfrac{ab + cd}{ac + bd} + a^2d - bc^2$ when $a = -3$, $b = -4$, $c = 5$ and $d = 3$

> Be careful when substituting negative values and remember the priority of operations.

....

PROBLEM SOLVED!

3 Mary says that the value of $2x^3$ when $x = 3$ is 216. Is Mary correct? Give a reason for your answer.

> You will need brilliant problem-solving skills to succeed in GCSE – **get practising now!**

....

4 Using the values given in the table, show that the value of each expression is either 5 or 7.

Letter	a	b	c	d	e
Value	-5	3	-1	5	8

(a) $\sqrt{ab + de}$

....

....

(b) $e(d - b)^2 - a^2$

....

....

(c) $\dfrac{a^3 + 2a^2b}{d}$

....

....

(d) $\sqrt[3]{e} + ac$

....

....

5 Using $m = 7$, $n = -2$ and $p = 5$, work out the value of each expression and write them in order of size, smallest first.

$\dfrac{m^2 + n}{p}$ $(2m + n)(n + p)$ mnp $m + 2n + 3p$

....

The *n*th term

Guided

3 (a) What is the fourth term of the sequence with *n*th term $5n - 1$?

$5 \times 4 - 1 =$ ....

(b) What is the 10th term of the sequence with *n*th term $3n + 4$?

$3 \times 10 + 4 =$ ....

(c) Work out the first three terms of the sequence with *n*th term $4n + 1$.

$n = 1: 4 \times 1 + 1 =$ ....

$n = 2: 4 \times$ .... $+ 1 =$ ....

$n = 3:$ .... $\times$ .... $+ 1 =$ ....

(d) Is 45 in the sequence $5n + 1$? Explain your answer.

....

2 (a) What is the seventh term of the sequence with *n*th term $2n - 3$?

Substitute $n = 7$

....

(b) Work out the first three terms of the sequence with *n*th term $10n - 2$

....

(c) Work out the first five terms of the sequence with *n*th term $10 - 2n$.

....

(d) Is 49 in the sequence $5n - 1$? Explain your answer.

....

Guided

3 Work out the *n*th term of each sequence.

> For sequences involving fractions, work out the *n*th terms of the numerator and denominator separately. The *n*th term will be a fraction.

(a) 3, 5, 7, 9, ...

1   3,   5,   7,   9, ...

−2 +2 +2 +2

difference is

$+2 \to 2n$, 'zero' term is $3 - 2 = 1$,

so *n*th term is .... $n +$ ....

(b) 16, 13, 10, 7, ...

....

(c) $\dfrac{1}{3}, \dfrac{2}{5}, \dfrac{3}{7}, ...$

....

(d) $\dfrac{1}{4}, \dfrac{3}{7}, \dfrac{5}{10}, ...$

....

4 Match each sequence with its *n*th term.

(a) 2, 6, 10, 14, ...   (i) $-2n + 12$

(b) 2, 7, 12, 17, ...   (ii) $3n - 2$

(c) 1, 4, 7, 10, ...   (iii) $4n - 2$

(d) 10, 8, 6, 4, ...   (iv) $-5n + 26$

(e) 21, 16, 11, 6, ...   (v) $5n - 3$

> Work out the difference to give the coefficient of *n*. A decreasing sequence will involve −*n*.

Non-linear sequences

1 Sort these sequences into arithmetic, geometric or quadratic sequences.

> Arithmetic sequences increase or decrease by the same amount. Geometric sequences increase or decrease by multiplying or dividing by the same number. Quadratic sequences involve the term n^2.

A 1, 3, 9, 27, ...   B 2, 5, 10, 17, ...   C 3, 6, 9, 12, ...

D 2, 5, 8, 11, ...   E 1, 10, 100, 1000, ...   F 1, 4, 9, 16, ...

Arithmetic: ....   Geometric: ....   Quadratic: ....

2 Is 110 in the sequence n^2? Give a reason for your answer.

....

3 Write down the first five terms of each sequence using the nth term given.

(a) $3n^2 - 2$ ....

(b) $\dfrac{n^2}{2} + 10$ ....

(c) $(n + 5)(n - 3)$ ....

> Guided

4 Work out the nth term of each sequence by comparing it with n^2.

(a) 0, 3, 8, 15, ...   1   4   9   16 nth term is $n^2 -$ ......

                                         $\Big)-1$

                    0   3   8   15

> Write out the first four terms of n^2. Compare each new sequence, term by term.

(b) 2, 8, 18, 32, ... 1   4   9   16 nth term is ......n^2

                                         $\Big)\times$ ......

                    2   8   18   32

5 Work out the nth term of each sequence by comparing it with n^2.

(a) 0.1, 0.4, 0.9, ...

....

(b) −1, 2, 7, 14, ...

....

(c) 5, 8, 13, 20, ...

....

(d) 4, 10, 20, 34, ...

....

6 Work out the nth term of this sequence. −8, −5, 0, 7, ...

....

Solving simple equations

Guided

1 Solve

(a) $5x + 7 = 47$ (-7)

$5x = 47 - 7$

$= 40$ $(\div 5)$

$x = $ ....

(b) $\frac{y}{3} - 2 = 6$ $(+2)$

$\frac{y}{3} = $ .... $(\times 3)$

$y = $ ....

> When using inverse operations, remember to do the same thing to both sides.

2 Solve

(a) $7z - 4 = 31$

$z = $ ....

(b) $15 - 3x = 6$

$x = $ ....

> Sometimes you need more than one step to solve an equation. Do one step at a time.

(c) $\frac{q}{3} + 7 = 10$

$q = $ ....

(d) $\sqrt{x} + 3 = 5$

$x = $ ....

PROBLEM SOLVED!

3 Sam thinks of a number. He multiplies it by 5 and then subtracts 7. The answer is 23. Write and solve an equation to work out Sam's number.

> You will need brilliant problem-solving skills to succeed in GCSE – **get practising now!**

....

Guided

4 Solve

(a) $5x - 4 = 3x + 8$ $(-3x)$

$2x - 4 = 8$ $(+4)$

$2x = 12$ $(\div 2)$

$x = $ ....

(b) $12 - 4y = 5y + 3$ $(+4y)$

$12 = 9y + 3$ (-3)

$9y = $ .... $(\div 9)$

$y = $ ....

> Do the same operation to both sides so that you get the unknown on one side. Then solve in the usual way.

5 Solve

(a) $20 - 5a = 11 - 2a$

$a = $ ....

(b) $4y + 11 = 6y - 3$

$y = $ ....

(c) $15 - 8x = 4x - 9$

$x = $ ....

6 Juan and Marta start with the same number. Juan trebles the number and adds 10. Marta multiplies the number by 5 and subtracts 2. They get the same answer. What number did they start with?

> Write an equation with Juan's number on one side and Marta's on the other. Solve the equation.

....

7 The total area of this shape is 67 cm². Work out the value of n.

6 cm

3 cm

n cm

n cm

> Write an equation for the area and solve by finding the square root.

$n = $ ....

Solving complex equations

1 Solve

| Expand any brackets first. |

(a) $5(2x - 3) = 55$

$10x - 15 = 55$ $(+15)$

$10x = \ldots\ldots\ldots\ldots$ $(\div 10)$

$x = \ldots\ldots\ldots\ldots$

(b) $3(10 - 2x) = -18$

$30 - 6x = -18$ $(+6x)$

$30 = 6x - 18$ $(+18)$

$6x = \ldots\ldots\ldots\ldots$

$x = \ldots\ldots\ldots\ldots$

(c) $4(5x - 6) = 3(6x + 4)$

$20x - 24 = \ldots\ldots\ldots\ldots$

$\ldots\ldots\ldots\ldots\ldots\ldots\ldots\ldots\ldots$

$\ldots\ldots\ldots\ldots\ldots\ldots\ldots\ldots\ldots$

$x = \ldots\ldots\ldots\ldots$

2 Solve $3(2x + 5) = 5(4x - 3)$

| Write your answer as a mixed number. |

$x = \ldots\ldots\ldots\ldots$

3 Solve

 | x is a negative mixed number. |

(a) $\dfrac{23 - 2x}{3} = 3x - 7$ $(\times 3)$

$23 - 2x$

$23 - 2x = 9x - 21$ $(+2x)$

$23 = \ldots\ldots\ldots\ldots\ldots\ldots\ldots\ldots\ldots\ldots\ldots$

$\ldots\ldots\ldots\ldots\ldots\ldots\ldots\ldots\ldots\ldots\ldots\ldots\ldots\ldots$

$x = \ldots\ldots\ldots\ldots$

(b) $\dfrac{3x - 2}{4} = 2x + 5$

$= 3(3x - 7)$

$x = \ldots\ldots\ldots\ldots$

4 Solve

| Factorise the quadratic, set each bracket equal to 0, and solve each equation. |

(a) $x^2 + 2x - 8 = 0$

$(x + 4)(x - \ldots\ldots\ldots\ldots) = 0$

$x + 4 = 0$ or $\ldots\ldots\ldots\ldots = 0$

$x = \ldots\ldots\ldots\ldots$ or $x = \ldots\ldots\ldots\ldots$

(b) $x^2 - 8x + 15 = 0$

$(\ldots\ldots\ldots\ldots)(\ldots\ldots\ldots\ldots) = 0$

$\ldots\ldots\ldots\ldots = 0$ or $\ldots\ldots\ldots\ldots = 0$

$x = \ldots\ldots\ldots\ldots$ or $x = \ldots\ldots\ldots\ldots$

5 Solve

| Quadratics of the form $(x + a)^2$ and $(x - a)^2$ have only one solution. |

(a) $x^2 + 9x + 20 = 0$

(b) $x^2 - 12x + 36 = 0$

(c) $x^2 - 81 = 0$

$\ldots\ldots\ldots\ldots\ldots\ldots\ldots\ldots$ $\ldots\ldots\ldots\ldots\ldots\ldots\ldots\ldots$ $\ldots\ldots\ldots\ldots\ldots\ldots\ldots\ldots$

6 A square with sides 6 cm is cut out of a square card with sides y cm.
The area of the remaining card is 64 cm^2.
What is the value of y?

| Write an equation for the area of the card that is left. Solve it to work out the value of y. |

y cm

6 cm
6 cm y cm

$y = \ldots\ldots\ldots\ldots$

Writing and solving equations

1 Write an equation and solve each word problem.

> Use *s* for the length of a side. A pentagon has five sides.

   (a) The perimeter of a regular pentagon is 45 cm. How long is one of its sides?

..............................cm

   (b) A regular 12-sided shape has a perimeter of 48 cm. How long is one of its sides?

..............................cm

2 A rectangle with width $2x + 4$ and length $2x - 2$ has a perimeter of 48 cm. What are the length and the width of the rectangle?

> Write an equation for the perimeter and solve for *x*. Then substitute your value for *x* into the expressions given for the length and the width.

$48 = (2x + 4) + (2x + 4) + (2x - 2) + (2x - 2)$

$ = \ ....$

$x = \ ....$

Width = ...cm   Length = ...cm

3 Work out the size of each angle.

> Write an equation using the fact that the angles in a triangle add up to 180°.

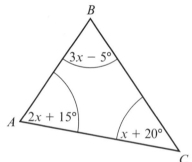

Angle A = ...°

Angle B = ...°

Angle C = ...°

> You will need brilliant problem-solving skills to succeed in GCSE – **get practising now!**

4 A square with sides $5x$ cm has an area of 1600 cm². Work out the length of each side.

> Write an equation, using the formula for the area of a square: area = side × side.

$5x$ cm

Area = 1600 cm²

> You will need brilliant problem-solving skills to succeed in GCSE – **get practising now!**

..............................cm

5 The angles on a line are given as $5x$, $3x - 40°$ and $2x + 20°$. What is the size of each angle?

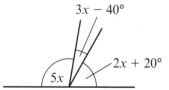

> Write an equation, using the fact that angles on a straight line add up to 180°.

....

6 A square with sides of length $3x$ cm has area of 324 cm². What is the perimeter of the square?

..............................cm

Inequalities

Guided

1 Write the inequalities shown by the number lines.

> An open circle means the number is **not** included; a closed circle means the number **is** included.

(a)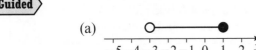

$-3 < x \leqslant$ ....

(b)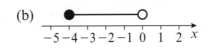

....

(c)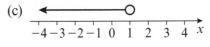

....

Guided

2 (a) Show these inequalities on the number lines.

> Look carefully at the signs: $<$ means the number is **not** included and $\leqslant$ means it **is** included.

(i) $-4 \leqslant x < 2$ (ii) $-2 \leqslant x \leqslant 1$ (iii) $x \leqslant 3$

(b) List the integer values of x for each inequality.

(i) $-4, -3,$ ....   (ii) ....   (iii) ....

Guided

3 Solve the inequalities.

> Solve in the same way as you would solve an equation. Check that you write the inequality signs correctly.

(a) $5x - 9 > 21$ $(+9)$

$5x > 21 + 9$

$x > 30$ $(\div 5)$

$x >$ ....

(b) $6 - 3x \leqslant 18$ (-6)

$-3x \leqslant 12$ $(..............)$

$-x \leqslant 4$ $(\times -1)$

$x \geqslant$ ....

4 Solve the inequalities.

(a) $3x + 7 \leqslant 34$ (b) $\dfrac{4x}{9} \geqslant -4$ (c) $5 - 2x < 17$

....

5 Write the integer values that satisfy both $5x - 3 > 12$ and $3x - 7 \leqslant 14$

> Solve both inequalities and write the integer values for each to see which numbers are in both.

....

33

Inequalities on graphs

Guided

1   Show on graph paper the region that satisfies the inequalities
$y \leqslant x$, $y > x - 4$ and $-1 \leqslant x < 5$

> Draw each line on the diagram. Use a dotted line for < (not included values) and a solid line for ≤ (included values). Draw an arrow to show which side of the line the region belongs. Shade the overlap between the regions.

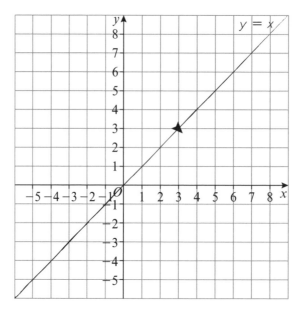

2   Show on graph paper the inequalities $-2 < x \leqslant 3$ and $-4 < y \leqslant 1$.
Shade the region that is satisfied by both inequalities.

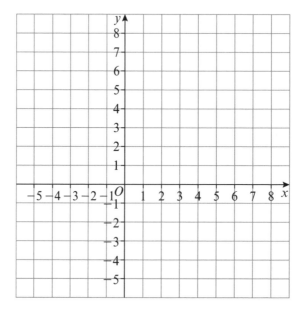

Simultaneous equations

Guided

1 Solve each pair of simultaneous equations.

(a) $2x + 4y = 32$ ①

  $2x - 3y = 11$ ②

> Label the equations ① and ②. Eliminate the term in x by subtracting ② from ①. Solve for y and use this value to solve for x.

  ① − ②: $2x + 4y - (2x - 3y) = 32 - 11$

  $7y = 21$

  $y = 3$

  Substitute $y = 3$ into ①: $2x + 4 \times$ .... $= 32$

  $2x =$ ....

  $x =$ ....

  Check using ②: $2 \times$ .... $- 3 \times$ .... $= 11$

  .... $= 11$

(b) $y = 5x$ ①

  $3x + y = 64$ ②

> Eliminate the term in y by substituting ① into ② and solve for x. Use this value to solve for y.

  Substitute ① into ②: $3x + 5x = 64$

  $x =$ ....

  Substitute $x =$ .... into ①:

  $y = 5 \times$ ....

    $=$ ....

  Check: ....

2 Solve each pair of simultaneous equations.

(a) $5x - 2y = 29$

  $3x + 4y = 7$

> Double the first equation.

(b) $3x + 4y = 25$

    $y = 2x - 2$

....

PROBLEM SOLVED!

3 5 apples and 3 bananas cost £1.50. 6 apples and 5 bananas cost £2.15. How much does 1 apple cost and how much does 1 banana cost?

> Write the problem as a pair of simultaneous equations with the totals in pence.

> You will need brilliant problem-solving skills to succeed in GCSE – **get practising now!**

1 apple costs ....p   1 banana costs ....p

4 A school uses large benches and small benches to seat their students in the hall. 4 large benches and 3 small benches seat 47 students. 5 large benches and 4 small benches seat 60 students. How many students can each type of bench seat?

1 large bench seats .... students   1 small bench seats .... students

Expression, equation, identity or formula?

1 Match each term with its definition.

A expression (i) An equation that is true for all values of the variables, shown using the $\equiv$ sign

B equation (ii) A mathematical rule showing the relationship between two or more variables

C formula (iii) Contains numbers, variables and operators but no equals sign

D identity (iv) Contains two expressions on either side of an equals sign

2 Write whether each of the following is an expression, an equation, a formula or an identity.

> Use the definitions in question 1 to help.

(a) $C = \pi d$

(b) $5x = 35$

(c) $(a + b)(a - b) = a^2 - b^2$

(d) $5x + 3y - 2$

....

(e) $3ab - 4c^2$

(f) $8x - 2 = 5x + 4$

(g) $D = \dfrac{M}{V}$

(h) $abc = bca$

....

3 (a) Substitute these pairs of values for a and b to show that $(a + b)^2 \equiv a^2 + 2ab + b^2$

> LHS = left-hand side of equals sign;
> RHS = right-hand side.

Guided

(i) $a = 2, b = 3$

LHS: $(2 + 3)^2 = 5^2 = $ ....

RHS: $2^2 + (2 \times 2 \times 3) + 3^2 = $ .... + ... + ... = ... = LHS

(ii) $a = 5, b = 4$

(iii) $a = -6, b = -1$

(b) Use algebra to show that $(a + b)^2 \equiv a^2 + 2ab + b^2$

LHS $= (a + b)^2 = a^2 + 2ab + b^2 = $ RHS ✓

4 Show that $(a - b)^2 \equiv a^2 - 2ab + b^2$

> Substitute three or more pairs of values for a and b or use algebra.

5 Prove that $(a - b)^2 \not\equiv a^2 - b^2$

Rearranging formulae

1 $D = \dfrac{M}{V}$ is a formula that shows the relationship between density (D), mass (M) and volume (V).

> You can substitute the values given for D and V and solve for M, or you can rearrange the formula to make V the subject first and then substitute.

Work out

(a) the value of M when $D = 15$ and $V = 8$

$$D = \frac{M}{V} \text{ so } 15 = \frac{M}{8}$$

$$M = 15 \times 8 = \text{...............}$$

(b) the value of V when $M = 200$ and $D = 25$

$$D = \frac{M}{V} \text{ so } 25 = \frac{200}{V}$$

$$V = \frac{200}{\text{.........}} = \text{...............}$$

2 Rearrange each formula to make the letter in brackets the subject.

(a) $5a + 8 = b$ $[a]$

$5a = \text{...............}$

$a = \text{...............}$

(b) $y = x^2$ $[x]$

$x = \sqrt{\text{...............}}$

(c) $b = 3t^2$ $[t]$

$t^2 = \text{...............}$

$t = \text{...............}$

> Use the same strategies as for solving equations to get the letter in brackets on its own on one side of the equals sign.

3 Rearrange each formula to make the letter in brackets the subject.

(a) $2y + 3x = 20$ $[x]$

(b) $3p - 5 = \dfrac{2q}{r}$ $[q]$

(c) $a = \dfrac{\sqrt{b + c}}{5}$ $[b]$

$x = \text{...........................}$

$q = \text{...........................}$

$b = \text{...........................}$

4 Rearrange each formula to make x the subject.

(a) $ax + 8 = 12 - bx$

$ax + bx = 12 - 8$

$x(a + b) = \text{...............}$

$x = \text{...........................}$

(b) $5xp - 4q = 3xq - 7p$

$x = \text{...........................}$

> Rearrange so the terms in x are on one side of the equals sign and then factorise to get x on its own.

PROBLEM SOLVED!

5 A company uses this formula when calculating their profit (in £):
Profit $= \frac{2}{7} \times$ sales $- 2000$

(a) Work out the company's profit when sales are worth £35 000.

> You will need brilliant problem-solving skills to succeed in GCSE – **get practising now!**

£...........................

(b) Work out the company's sales when its profit is £6000.

£...........................

6 The volume, V, of a cylinder is given by the formula $V = \pi r^2 h$ where r is the radius and h is the height.

(a) Make r the subject of the formula.

$r = \text{...........................}$

(b) Work out the radius of a cylinder with a volume of 1131 cm^2 and a height of 10 cm.
Give your answer to the nearest cm.

> Put brackets around 10π when using your calculator to work out r.

$r = \text{...........................}$ cm

Using formulae

Guided

PROBLEM SOLVED!

1   The formula for the surface area, A, of a cylinder is $A = 2\pi r^2 + 2\pi rh$ where r is the radius and h is the height. Work out to 2 d.p.

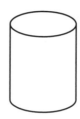

> Substitute the values given for r and h into the formula. Use the $\boxed{\pi}$ button on your calculator when calculating.

> You will need brilliant problem-solving skills to succeed in GCSE – **get practising now!**

(a) the surface area of a cylinder with a radius of 5 cm and a height of 9 cm

$A = 2 \times \pi \times 5^2 + 2 \times \pi \times 5 \times 9$

= .... + ... = ...cm²

(b) the height of a cylinder with a radius of 7 cm and surface area of 836 cm²

$836 = 2 \times \pi \times 7^2 + 2 \times \pi \times 7 \times h$
$\quad = 98\pi + 14\pi h$

$h = $ ....cm

Guided

2   Pythagoras' theorem states that $a^2 + b^2 = c^2$, where c is the hypotenuse of a right-angled triangle and a and b are the shorter sides.

> Substitute and then rearrange to solve for a.

Work out

(a) c when $a = 4$ cm and $b = 3$ cm   (b) a when $b = 12$ cm and $c = 15$ cm

$c^2 = $ .... + ... = ...

$c = \sqrt{\text{.........}} = $ ....cm

$a = $ ....cm

3   Substitute into the formula $a = bc^2$ to work out

(a) a when $b = 9$ and $c = 4$ (b) b when $a = 15$ and $c = 3$ (c) c when $a = 25$ and $b = 10$ (to 2 d.p.)

$a = $ .... $b = $ .... $c = $ ....

4   The volume, V, of a cylinder is given by the formula $V = \pi r^2 h$ where r is the radius and h is the height. Work out to 2 d.p.

(a) V when $r = 8$ cm and $h = 11$ cm

$V = $ ....cm³

(b) h when $r = 6.5$ cm and $V = 550$ cm³

$h = $ ....cm

(c) r when $h = 15$ cm and $V = 954$ cm³

$r = $ ....cm

Writing formulae

1 A tutor charges £24 per hour plus £2 for materials.

(a) Write a formula to describe the tutor's total charge £C for h hours' work.

C = ... h + ...

(b) A student has a 3.5-hour revision session. How much does he pay?

C = 3.5 × .... + ... = £..............

(c) Another student pays the tutor £50. How long was the tuition session?

50 = ... h + ...

.... h = 50 − ....

h = ... hours

> For part (c), you can substitute first or rearrange so that h is the subject and then substitute.

2 A window cleaner charges £9 to clean the windows of a large house and £7 to clean the windows of a small house.

(a) Write a formula to describe her total charge C (in pounds) to clean the windows of L large houses and S small houses.

....

(b) What is her income from cleaning the windows of 6 large houses and 10 small houses?

£............................

(c) One day she earns £99. On that day she cleaned the windows of 4 large houses. How many small houses did she clean windows for?

.... small houses

3 The mass of a small box is 120 g and the mass of a large box is 150 g.

(a) Write a formula for the total mass (M) of S small boxes and L large boxes.

....

(b) What is the total mass of 8 small boxes and 5 large boxes? Give your answer in kg.

.... kg

(c) Jean has 10 large boxes and some small boxes. The total mass is 1.98 kg. How many small boxes does Jean have?

> In part (c), change kg to grams.

.... small boxes

4 A store sells cups for £2, bowls for £3 and plates for £2.50.

(a) Write a formula for the total cost, T (in pounds), of c cups, b bowls and p plates.

....

(b) Sarah buys 12 of each. What is the total cost?

£............................

(c) Elias buys the same number of cups, bowls and plates. He pays £37.50. How many of each item does he buy?

.... of each

Midpoint and gradient

1 (a) Write the coordinates of

   (i) point M (1, 3)   (ii) point N (.............., ...)

> You show coordinates like this: (x, y).

(b) P is the midpoint of the line segment MN.

   Write the coordinates of the point P.   (.............., ...)

> The midpoint of a line segment is exactly halfway along the line.

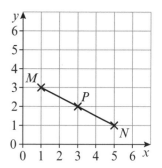

2 Work out the coordinates of the midpoint of the line segment joining (0, 6) and (10, 12).

> The coordinates of the midpoint of a line segment are $\left(\dfrac{(x_1 + x_2)}{2}, \dfrac{(y_1 + y_2)}{2}\right)$

$$\left(\frac{0 + 10}{2}, \frac{.............. + ...}{2}\right) = (.............., ...)$$

3 Work out the coordinates of the midpoint of the line segment joining

(a) $(-2, 4)$ and $(6, 8)$ (b) $(4, -7)$ and $(6, -1)$

....

4 Find the gradient of

(a) line A

> A line sloping down, left to right, will have a negative gradient.

$$\text{Gradient} = \frac{\text{distance up}}{\text{distance across}} = \frac{4}{2} = ...$$

(b) line B

$$\text{Gradient} = \frac{\text{distance up}}{\text{distance across}} = \frac{..........}{..........}$$

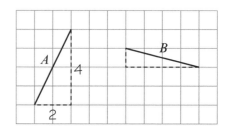

5 Find the gradient of

> Choose two points on the line with whole-number coordinates and draw a right-angled triangle.

(a) line C (b) line D

....

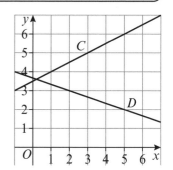

y = mx + c

1 (a) Work out the gradient of the straight line.

Gradient = $\dfrac{\text{distance up}}{\text{distance across}}$ = $\dfrac{\text{............}}{\text{............}}$ = ...

(b) Write the y-intercept of this graph.

> The y-intercept is the point where the line crosses the y-axis.

y-intercept is ....

(c) Write the equation of the straight line.

> The equation of a straight line is y = mx + c, where m is the gradient and c is the y-intercept.

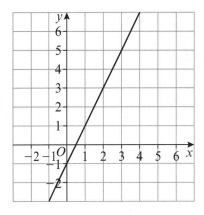

....

2 Find the equation of this straight line.

> The line slopes down from left to right.

....

3 (a) The equation of the vertical line is x = 2

On the grid draw and label a line with equation x = 4

(b) The equation of the horizontal line is y = 3

On the grid draw and label a line with equation y = −1

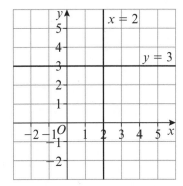

4 Match each equation with its line.

(a) y = 4   ....

(b) $y = \frac{1}{2}x - 1$ ....

(c) y = −x + 2   ....

(d) x = −2   ....

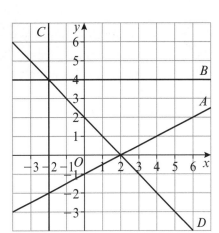

Straight-line graphs

Guided

1 (a) Complete this table of values for the graph of
       $y = 3x + 1$ for values of x from 0 to 4.

x	0	1	2	3	4
y	1				

$x = 0$: $y = (3 \times 0) + 1$
$\quad\quad = 0 + 1 = 1$

> Substitute the x value into the equation.

$x = 1$: $y = (3 \times 1) + 1$

$\quad\quad = \text{..............} + \text{..............} = \text{..............}$

$x = 2$: $y = 3 \times \text{..............} + 1$

$\quad\quad = \text{..............} + \text{..............} = \text{..............}$

$x = 3$: $y = 3 \times \text{..............} + \text{..............}$

$\quad\quad = \text{..............} + \text{..............} = \text{..............}$

$x = 4$: $y = \text{..............} \times \text{..............} + \text{..............} = \text{..............}$

(b) On the grid, draw the graph of $y = 3x + 1$.

> Plot each point on the grid. Use a ruler to draw a straight line through the points.

2 Draw the graph of $y + x = 6$ for values of x from 0 to 6.

> Draw a table of values. Use x values from 0 to 6.

x	0	1	2	3	4	5	6
y							

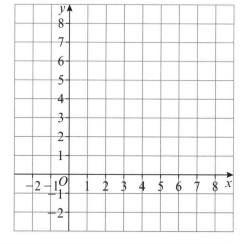

3 Draw the graph of $y = \frac{1}{2}x + 2$ for values of x from -2 to 3 without using a table of values.

> Compare the equation with $y = mx + c$ to identify the gradient and the y-intercept. Mark the y-intercept and then use the gradient to move across and up. Be careful – this graph has a fractional gradient.

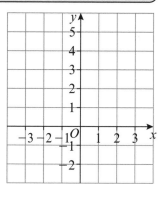

Parallel and perpendicular

1 Which of these straight lines are parallel?

> Rearrange equations *C* and *D* so they are in the form $y = mx + c$.

A $y = 4x + 3$ B $y = 3x + 4$ C $2y = 4x + 5$ D $2y = 8x + 10$ ....

2 Write the equation of a straight line parallel to $y = 4 - 5x$.

....

3 A straight line has the equation $y = 2x + 5$.

Guided

(a) Is the point $(3, 11)$ on the line?

> A point with coordinates (x, y) is on a given line if, when you substitute the given values for x and y into the equation, the statement is true. Substitute $x = 3$ and $y = 11$ into $y = 2x + 5$.

....

(b) Another line goes through the points $A(2, 5)$ and $B(4, 9)$. Is this line parallel to $y = 2x + 5$? Explain your answer.

Gradient of line between A and $B = \dfrac{\text{distance up}}{\text{distance across}} = \dfrac{9 - \text{............}}{4 - \text{............}} = \dfrac{\text{............}}{\text{............}} = \dfrac{\text{............}}{\text{............}}$

The gradient of the line $y = 2x + 5$ is ....

The gradients of the lines are .... so the lines are ....

4 (a) Circle the gradient of a line perpendicular to the line $y = 4x + 1$.

> If a line has a gradient of m, the perpendicular line will have a gradient of $-\dfrac{1}{m}$

   1   -4 $\frac{1}{4}$ $-\frac{1}{4}$ -1

(b) Circle the gradient of a line perpendicular to the line $y = -\frac{1}{3}x + 2$.

   2       $\frac{1}{3}$ 3 -3 -2

Guided

5 A straight line, L, has the equation $y = 7x + 2$. Write the equation of the straight line P which is parallel to L and passes through the point $(0, -3)$.

> Use the point $(0, -3)$ to identify the y-intercept of line P.

The gradient of L is ....

The gradient of P is ....

The equation of P is $y =$ .... $x +$ ....

PROBLEM SOLVED!

6 A straight line, L, has the equation $y = \frac{1}{2}x + 4$. Write the equation of the straight line P which is perpendicular to L and passes through the point $(0, 6)$.

> You will need brilliant problem-solving skills to succeed in GCSE – get practising now!

....

Formulae from graphs and tables

Guided

1 A taxi driver charges £3 for each km travelled plus a fixed charge of £2.

> Substitute the values for *d* into your formula and complete the table.

(a) Write a formula for the amount *P* (in pounds) she charges to travel *d* km.

$P = $ .... $d + $ ....

(b) Complete the table of values for the first 4 km of a journey.

Distance, *d* (km)	0	1	2	3	4
Charge, *P* (£)					

$d = 0$: $P = (3 \times 0) + 2 = $ .... $+ 2 = $ ....

$d = 1$: $P = (3 \times $ ....$) + 2 = $ .... $+ 2 = $ ....

$d = 2$: $P = ($.............. $\times$ ....$) + $ .... $= $ .... $+ $ .... $= $ ....

$d = 3$: ....

$d = 4$: ....

(c) Plot a graph of this information on the axes.

(d) A taxi fare is £10.
Use your graph to estimate the distance travelled.

..............km

> Find £10 on the vertical axis and read across to your line and then down to the horizontal axis.

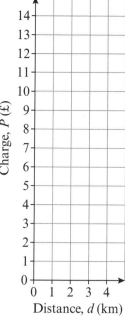

2 The graph shows an electrician's charge, *P*, for his work.

(a) Write a formula for the electrician's charge.

> Work out the gradient of the line and the value of any initial fee. Use these to write a formula beginning $P = ...$

....

(b) The electrician earns £140. For how many hours does he work?

...........................hours

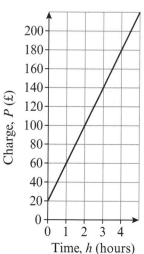

Charge, *P* (£)

Time, *h* (hours)

Quadratic graphs

1 (a) Complete the table of values for $y = x^2 + 2x$.

x	−3	−2	−1	0	1	2
y	3					

$x = -3: y = (-3)^2 + (2 \times -3) = 9 - 6 = 3$

$x = -2: y = (-2)^2 + (2 \times -2) = 4 - 4 = \dots\dots$

$x = -1: y = (-1)^2 + (2 \times -1) = \dots\dots = \dots\dots$

$x = 0: y = (\dots\dots)^2 + (2 \times \dots\dots) = \dots\dots$

$x = 1: y = (\dots\dots)^2 + (\dots\dots\dots) = \dots\dots$

$x = 2: y = \dots\dots\dots\dots\dots\dots = \dots\dots$

(b) On the grid, plot the graph of $y = x^2 + 2x$.

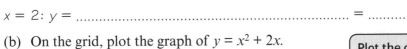

Plot the coordinates from your table on the grid and join with a smooth curve.

(c) What are the coordinates of the turning point?

....

(d) Is the turning point a maximum or a minimum?

....

(e) Write the equation of the line of symmetry.

....

2 (a) Complete the table of values for $y = x^2 - 2x - 3$.

x	−2	−1	0	1	2	3	4
y							

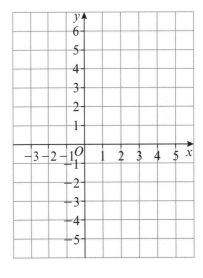

(b) On the grid, plot the graph of $y = x^2 - 2x - 3$.

(c) What are the coordinates of the turning point?

....

(d) Is the turning point a maximum or a minimum?

....

(e) Write the equation of the line of symmetry.

....

Other non-linear graphs

Guided

1 (a) Complete the table of values for $y = x^3 + 2$.

x	−2	−1	0	1	2
y	−6				

$x = -2$: $(-2)^3 + 2 = -8 + 2 = 6$

$x = -1$: $(-1)^3 + 2 = -1 + 2 = $ ....

$x = 0$: $(0)^3 + 2 = $ .... $+ 2 = $ ....

$x = 1$: $($..............$)^3 + $ .... $= $ .... $= $ ....

$x = 2$: .... $= $ ....

(b) On the grid, draw the graph of $y = x^3 + 2$

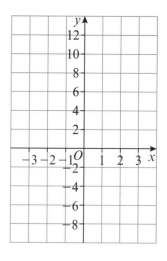

2 (a) Complete this table of values for $y = \dfrac{4}{x}$.

x	0.5	1	1.5	2	2.5	3	3.5	4
y								

> Round your answers to 1 decimal place to plot the coordinates.

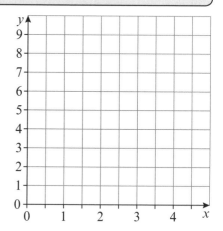

(b) On the grid, draw the graph of $y = \dfrac{4}{x}$.

3 Match each equation to a possible graph.

> Look at the shape of each curve. Cubic graphs have a kink, reciprocal graphs have two symmetrical parts and exponential graphs increase at an increasing rate.

(a) $y = \dfrac{5}{x}$ (b) $y = 2 - x^3$ (c) $y = x^3 + 3x$ (d) $y = 2^x$

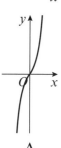

A

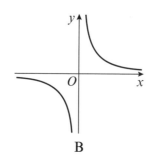

B

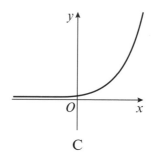

C

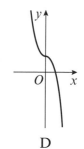

D

Real-life graphs

1 (a) What does this graph show?

It converts between ....

and ....

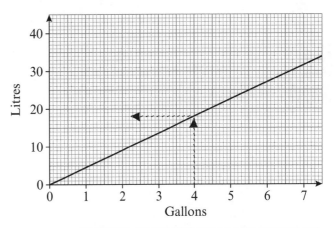

(b) What does each small square represent
on the horizontal (gallons) axis?

> There are 10 small squares for 1 gallon, so
> 1 small square represents $\frac{1}{10}$th of 1 gallon.

0............... gallons

(c) Use the graph to convert 4 gallons to the nearest litre.

.... litres

(d) Convert 25 litres to gallons and the nearest tenth of a gallon.

.... gallons

(e) Which is the larger capacity, 2.4 gallons or 12 litres? Explain how the graph shows this.

....

2 The graph shows the average
exchange rate for converting
£1 to euros (€) for the years
2009 to 2015.

(a) In which year between 2009
and 2015 was the exchange
rate at its lowest?

....

(b) Over which consecutive
2-year period did the
exchange rate increase
most rapidly?

....

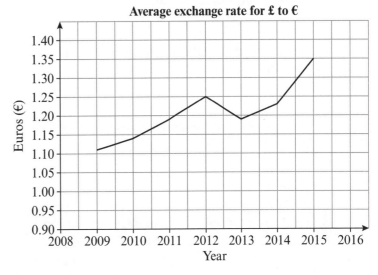

Average exchange rate for £ to €

(c) What was the approximate exchange rate in

(i) 2012 ....   (ii) 2011? ....

(d) How much more did a person receive for £1 in 2014 than in 2010?

€ ....

(e) Explain why you cannot say from this graph what the exchange rate was in 2008 or predict
with confidence what it will be in 2016.

....

....

Algebra problem-solving

Guided

PROBLEM SOLVED!

1 (a) Write an equation for the sum of the angles in the quadrilateral.

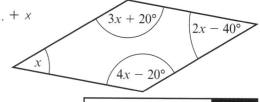

The angles in a quadrilateral add up to 360°.

$(3x + 20)$ + ... + ... + x

= .... − ....

= ....

(b) Solve the equation to find the value of x.

.... − .... = ...

You will need brilliant problem-solving skills to succeed in GCSE – **get practising now!**

....

(c) Work out the size of each angle.

Substitute the value of x into each expression.

x = ... $3x + 20$ $2x − 40$ $4x − 20$

= ....   = ...   = ...

= ....   = ...   = ...

(d) What type of quadrilateral could this be? Explain your answer.

....

2 Use the graph to answer the questions.

(a) What was the average temperature in October?

.... °C

(b) Which months had the lowest daytime temperature?

....

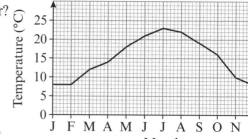

Average daytime temperature, London 2014

(c) How does the graph show the hottest month?

....

(d) What trends does the graph show?

....

(e) The formula for changing from degrees Celsius (°C) to degrees Fahrenheit (°F) is $F = \frac{9}{5}C + 32$. Use the formula and the graph to give the November temperature in degrees Fahrenheit.

Read the temperature in °C for November from the graph. Use the formula to convert it to °F.

.... °F

3 At a cafe, Liz spends £9.50 buying 3 coffees and 4 teas and Phil spends £9.75 buying 4 coffees and 3 teas. What is the cost of 1 coffee and the cost of 1 tea?

Use simultaneous equations.

Coffee: £............................   Tea: £............................

Ratio

4 Write each ratio in its simplest form.

> Always write the ratio in the order asked for. To simplify fully, divide by the highest common factor.

(a) A garment label says '75% cotton, 25% polyester'. What is the ratio of cotton to polyester?

cotton : polyester = 75 : 25 = ... : ....

(b) A recipe uses 125 g of sugar to 175 g of butter. What is the ratio of sugar to butter?

.... : .... = ... : .... = ... : ....

2 Divide £450 in the ratio 7 : 2.

> Add the parts of the ratio to find the total number of parts. Then divide the amount by the number of parts to find the value of **one** part. Finally, multiply each number in the ratio by the value of one part. Check your answer.

7 + 2 = 9   450 ÷ 9 = ...

7 × .... = £.....................   2 × .... = £.....................

Check: .... + ... = £450

3 At a pre-school, the ratio of boys to girls is 5 : 6. There are 22 children.
How many are boys and how many are girls?

.... boys   .... girls

4 In a bag of snack mix the ratio of walnuts to dried fruit to pecans is 5 : 2 : 1. There are 20 g of dried fruit. How many grams of snack mix are in the bag?

> Work out the mass of one part, then multiply by the total number of parts.

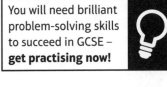

> You will need brilliant problem-solving skills to succeed in GCSE – **get practising now!**

.... grams

5 Write each ratio in the form 1 : *n*.

> In part (c), convert 3 m to cm. In part (d), multiply by 100 first to get rid of the decimals.

(a) 30 : 300   (b) 5 : 9   (c) 25 cm : 3 m   (d) 0.75 : 1.2

....

6 Mark spends his monthly allowance on entertainment, clothes and snacks in the ratio 4 : 5 : 3. He spends £21 on snacks.

(a) How much does Mark spend on clothes?

£.............................

(b) How much is Mark's monthly allowance?

£.............................

Direct proportion

1 (a) 8 DVDs cost £136.
How much do 15 DVDs cost?

£136 ÷ 8 = £...............

15 × £.............. = £...............

> Work out the cost of 1 DVD (£136 ÷ 8) and then
> multiply to find the total cost of the given number.

(b) 40 seedlings cost £20.
How much do 25 seedlings cost?

£.............................

6 Work out the better value deal in each part. Show your working.

(a) 7 for £35 or 10 for £48

(b) 5 for £90 or 8 for £120

> Work out the cost of 1 item.

> You will need brilliant
> problem-solving skills
> to succeed in GCSE –
> **get practising now!**

PROBLEM SOLVED!

....

....

3 250 g of cheese costs £3.60.

(a) What is the price per kg?

£.............................

(b) How much will 150 g cost?

£.............................

4 On a particular day the exchange rate between Canadian dollars and pounds sterling was £1 = \$2.03.

(a) Sunil changed £320 into Canadian dollars. How many dollars did he get?

320 × .... = \$...........................

(b) Moira changed \$500 into pounds sterling. How much, to the nearest whole penny, did she receive?

£.............................

(c) Which is worth more, \$565 or £280? Show your working.

....

5 1 kg = 2.2 pounds approximately.

(a) Change 5.8 kg into pounds.

.... pounds

(b) Change 14.3 pounds into kg.

...........................kg

(c) There are 14 pounds in 1 stone.
What is 9 stone in kg, to the nearest kg?

> First work out how many pounds there are in 9 stone.

...........................kg

6 Which of these equations show(s) direct proportion?

A $y = 3x + 2$ B $y = 3x^2$ C $y = \dfrac{x}{3}$ D $y = \dfrac{3}{x}$

Inverse proportion

1 Which graph shows inverse proportion?

A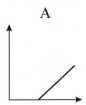

B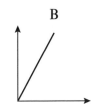

C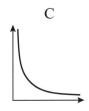

> If quantities are inversely proportional, as one increases the other decreases.

....

Guided

PROBLEM SOLVED!

2 It takes 3 electricians 2 days to wire up a new house. Working at the same rate and on identical houses, how long will it take

> You will need brilliant problem-solving skills to succeed in GCSE – **get practising now!**

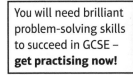

(a) 6 electricians to wire up one house?

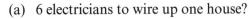

3 electricians × 2 days = ... days' work

.... days' work ÷ .... electricians = ... days

(b) 2 electricians to wire up the same house?

.... days' work ÷ .... electricians = ... days

> Work out the total number of days needed to complete the work. Then divide by the number of workers. Check that your answer makes sense: the more workers there are, the less time is needed.

3 It takes 3 people 8 hours to paint a room.

(a) How long it will take 4 people to paint the same room?

.... hours

(b) It takes 12 hours to paint the same room again. How many painters are there?

.... painters

Guided

4 Which of these pairs of x- and y-values are in inverse proportion to each other? Complete the table to show how you know.

	x	y	xy
A	2.4	10	2.4 × .... = ...
B	2.5	9.24	
C	2.2	10.5	
D	3.2	7.5	

> If they are in inverse proportion, their products will be the same.

....

5 A running club wants to raise money to buy some new racing vests for their junior members. The vests cost £240 in total.

(a) Four runners have offered to raise £60 each. Complete the table to show how much money other numbers of runners would each need to raise.

(b) Does this example show inverse proportion? Explain your answer.

Runners	Amount
4	£240 ÷ 4 = £60
5	
6	
8	
10	

....

Maps and scales

Guided

1 A model of a building uses a scale of 1 cm = 12 m.

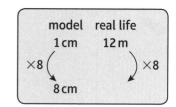

(a) The height of the model is 8 cm.
Work out the height of the building.

8 × .... = ... metres

(b) The width of the building is 78 m. Work out the width of the model.

78 ÷ .... = ... cm

2 A map uses a scale of 1 : 20 000.

(a) The distance on the map between the school and the train
station is 6 cm. What is the distance in real life?
Give your answer in kilometres.

> 1 : 20 000 means
> 1 cm = 20 000 cm = 200 m
> 1 km = 1000 m

.... km

(b) The distance between the train station and the town hall is 1 km in real life.
Work out the distance between them on the map.

.... cm

3 A model of Windsor Castle is made to a scale of 1 cm : 4 m.
The actual castle is 19.84 m in height. What is the height of the model?

.... cm

4 The diagram shows a scale
drawing of the attractions
in a park.

(a) Work out the distance in
real life between the
playground and the lake.

.... m

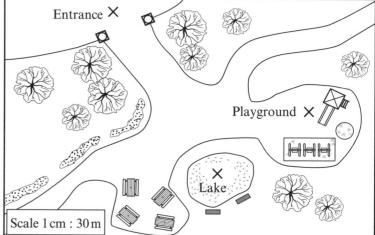

(b) Robert says that the distance
from the entrance to the
playground is less than
200 m.
Is Robert correct?
Use the map to explain your answer.

....

(c) A bus station is outside the park and is 120 m from the lake.
Mark a possible position of the bus station.

.... cm

Speed, distance, time

1 A car travels 140 km in 2 hours. Calculate its average speed in km/h.

Speed = distance ÷ time

= .... ÷ ....

= .... km/h

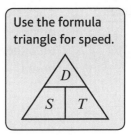

Use the formula triangle for speed.

$\frac{D}{S \mid T}$

2 Simon cycled 10 km in 30 minutes.
Work out Simon's average speed in km/h.

Make sure your units match.
Convert 30 minutes into hours.

.... km/h

3 A train travels at an average speed of 90 mph.
The journey from London to Manchester takes 2 hours and 30 minutes.
Calculate the distance from London to Manchester in miles.

2 hours and 30 minutes = ... hours

Distance = speed × time

= .... × .... = ... miles

4 A horse gallops at an average speed of 12 km/h for 1 hour and 15 minutes.
Calculate the distance in km the horse galloped in that time.

.... km

5 A plane travels at an average speed of 550 mph.
How long does it take to travel 1925 miles?
Give your answer in hours and minutes.

Time = distance ÷ speed

.... hours and .... minutes

6 Jason leaves his house at 7.45 am and walks to school,
arriving at 8.30 am.
He walks at an average speed of 8 km/h.
How far is his house from the school?

First, work out the time it takes
him to walk to school in hours.

.... km

Distance–time graphs

Guided

1 The graph shows Max's family trip to see his grandparents. They stopped for a short break on the way, spent some time there and then returned home.

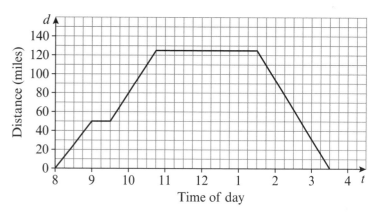

(a) How far away from Max's home do his grandparents live? ....

(b) How many miles were travelled in total on this journey? ....

(c) How long did they spend with his grandparents?

> For part (c), check the scale on the horizontal axis carefully.

....

(d) At what time did the return journey start? ....

(e) What was their speed during the first part of the journey?

speed = distance ÷ time = ... ÷ .... = ... mph

(f) What was their speed during the return journey? ....

(g) In which section of the journey was Max's family travelling fastest? How does the graph show this?

....

2 Josh and his friends walked from his house to a park to have a picnic. The graph shows information about their walk.

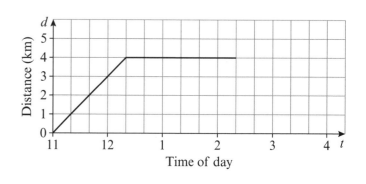

(a) How far from Josh's home did they have their picnic? ....

(b) What was their walking speed? ....

(c) How long did they spend at the picnic site? ....

(d) They walked home at the same speed as they walked to the park. Complete the distance–time graph to show this.

(e) Use the completed graph to work out what time they got home. ....

54

Density

Guided

1 Write the formula you need to find each missing quantity.
Then write the correct units for the missing quantity. Choose from:

g   cm   cm³   kg   g/cm³   m³   m   kg/m³

Use the formula triangle for density.

M / D | V

(a) Mass, when given density and volume $M = D \times$ ....   g or kg

(b) Density, when given volume and mass $D =$ .... ÷ .... or ....

(c) Volume, when given density and mass $V =$ .... or ....

2 A glass statue has a mass of 7850 kg and a volume of 2.5 m³.
What is its density?

Use the formulae from Q1.

..............................kg/m³

PROBLEM SOLVED!

3 (a) The density of brass is 8.394 g/cm³.
What is the volume of a brass paperweight with a mass of 750 g, to the nearest cm³?

You will need brilliant problem-solving skills to succeed in GCSE – **get practising now!**

..............................cm³

(b) Tin has a density of 7.339 g/cm³.
What is the mass of a tin plate with a volume of 15 cm³, to the nearest gram?

.... grams

PROBLEM SOLVED!

4 (a) The density of gold is 1929 kg/m³.
Convert this density into g/cm³.

You will need brilliant problem-solving skills to succeed in GCSE – **get practising now!**

..............................g/cm³

(b) The density of zinc is 7.049 g/cm³.
Convert this density into kg/m³.

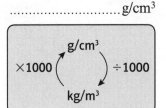
g/cm³
×1000 ÷1000
kg/m³

..............................kg/m³

5 (a) The density of olive oil is 0.913 g/cm³.
What is the mass of 500 ml of olive oil, to the nearest gram?

1 ml = 1 cm³

.... grams

(b) Pure water has a density of 1000 kg/m³.
Using your answer to part (a), will olive oil float or sink in pure water?
You must explain your answer.

Change 1000 kg/m³ into g/cm³. A material with a lower density will float on a material with a higher density.

....

Graphs of rates of change

Guided

1 Choose a phrase from each box to describe each graph.

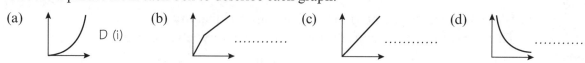

(a) ⟋ D (i)   (b) ⟋ ....   (c) ⟋ ....   (d) ⟋ ....

Description of rate of change	What the graph could be describing
A Rate of change is constant	(i) Filling a container that is narrower at the top
B Quick decrease at first, then slower	(ii) Converting between miles and km
C Varying rate: fast then slower	(iii) Depreciation in the value of a car
D Varying rate: slow then faster	(iv) Filling a container that is narrower at the bottom

2 Sketch a graph to show the water level in each container as it is filled with water flowing at a constant rate.

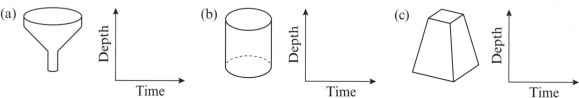

(a)   (b)   (c)

3 (a) Use the information in the table to draw a graph showing how the price of grain varies with its mass.

Mass	Price
100 g	50p
275 g	£1.25
350 g	£1.50
500 g	£2.25
1 kg	£3.50

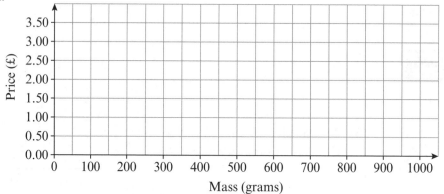

(b) Explain how your graph shows that the price of grain is not proportional to its mass.

....

Percentage change

1 Work out

> Use the decimal multiplier method. An increase of 2% = 100% + 2% = 102% = 1.02
> A decrease of 35% = 100% − 35% = 65% = 0.65

(a) £750 increased by 2%

750 × 1.02 = £.............................

(b) £1500 decreased by 35%

1500 × 0.65 = £.............................

(c) £2856 increased by 4.5%

= .... × .... = £.................

(d) £8482 decreased by 22%

= .... × .... = £.................

(e) 14% tax added to €3600

= .... = €.................

(f) 12.5% off £1200

= .... = £.................

PROBLEM SOLVED!

2 A bank is offering 3.5% interest on savings. Charles has saved £2800. How much will he have after the interest is added?

> 3.5% = 3.5 ÷ 100 = 0.035
> The interest is added so this is a percentage increase.

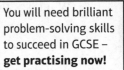

You will need brilliant problem-solving skills to succeed in GCSE – **get practising now!**

£.............................

3 The population of a town 100 years ago was 25 540. It has increased by 65%. What is the current population?

....

4 Two companies advertise the same 2-week holiday. Which company offers the better deal? Show your working out.

Company A: €1200 reduced by 25%   Company B: €1320 reduced by 33%

....

5 Jemma buys a ski jacket in a sale. The jacket costs $150 less 35%. She has to pay 12.5% tax on her purchase. How much does Jemma have to pay? Write your answer correct to 2 decimal places.

> First work out the sale price and then add on the 12.5% tax.

$.............................

Guided

6 (a) The value of a property has risen from £350 000 to £406 000. What percentage increase is this?

> % difference = $\dfrac{\text{difference}}{\text{original amount}} \times 100$

406 000 − 350 000 = ...

$\dfrac{............}{350\,000}$ = ...%

(b) In a sale, a pair of shoes has been reduced from £85 to £69. What is the percentage reduction, to the nearest per cent?

.............................%

Reverse percentages

Guided

1 (a) The total cost of a computer + 20% VAT is £576. What was the price of the computer before VAT was added?

576 ÷ 1.2 = £...........................

(b) In a 15% off sale, a coat costs £102. What was its original price before the sale?

102 ÷ 0.85 = £...........................

> Convert the percentage increase (or decrease) to a decimal multiplier. Then divide the new amount by the multiplier.
>
> Check that your answer makes sense. Should the original amount be more or less than the final amount?
>
> ×
>
> original → new
> amount   amount
>
> ÷

2 (a) After 15% tax has been added, the price of a book is $13.80. What was the price of the book before tax?

$...........................

(b) A jumper costs £33 after its price has been reduced in a sale by 45%. What was the price of the jumper before the sale?

£...........................

(c) The value of a motorbike has depreciated by 11%. It is now valued at £5340. What was its original value?

£...........................

(d) After interest of 3.5% has been added, Nicola has £558.90 in her bank account. How much money was in the account before the interest was added?

£...........................

3 In one year the population of a village increased by 7.5% to 258 people. What was its population at the start?

....

4 Mathieu made a 13% loss on the sale of his car. He sold it for £3132. How much did he pay for the car?

£...........................

5 A bank gives 2.25% simple interest on amounts invested for 3 years. After 3 years Jack has £3736.25. How much did Jack originally invest?

> Simple interest is calculated as a percentage of the original amount. After 3 years, the interest to be added is 3 × 2.25% × original amount.

£...........................

Compound interest

1 £2600 is invested at compound interest of 2% over 4 years.

(a) Complete the table to work out the interest for each year.
Round your answers to the nearest penny (2 d.p.).

Year	Starting balance (£)	Interest (£)	New balance (£)
1	2600	2600 × 0.02 = 52	2600 + 52 = 2652
2	2652		
3			
4			

(b) What is the new total balance after 4 years?   £............................

(c) How much interest was earned in total?   £............................

(d) Was more interest earned in years 1 and 2 or in years 3 and 4? Explain your answer.

....

2 Work out the final balance and
the interest on each amount.
Round your answers to the
nearest penny (2 d.p.).

(a) £3200 invested for 4 years
at 3% compound interest

Final balance: 3200 × (1.03)⁴ = £............................

Interest: .... − 3200 = £............................

(b) £5750 invested for 5 years at 3.5% compound interest

Final balance: 5750 × (............................)⁵ = £............................

Interest: .... − .... = £............................

You will need brilliant
problem-solving skills
to succeed in GCSE –
get practising now!

3 Hugh invests £3000 at 2.75% compound interest for 3 years.
Annie invests £3000 at 2.35% compound interest for 4 years.
Who will earn more interest on their investment?
Show your working.

You will need brilliant
problem-solving skills
to succeed in GCSE –
get practising now!

....

4 Ali bought a car 5 years ago. The value of Ali's car
has depreciated at an average of 7.5% per year.
He paid £17 500 for the car.
How much is it worth now? Give your answer to the nearest pound.

Depreciation means a loss, so the decimal
multiplier is less than 1. (1 − 0.075 = ☐)

£............................

5 Digital cameras are decreasing in price at an average rate of 17.5% per year. How many years
will it take for a £280 camera to cost **less** than £100? You must show your calculations.

.... years

Proportion problem-solving

1 Which box of cereal offers the best value?
You must show your calculations.

Box A, 500 g for £2.99   Box B, 375 g for £2.25   Box C, 750 g for £4.75

Box A: 299p ÷ 500 = ...p per gram

Box B: ....

Box C: ....

Box .... is the best value because ....

You will need brilliant problem-solving skills to succeed in GCSE – **get practising now!**

2 A bank is offering 2.4% simple interest or 2.3% compound interest on investments. Work out the better rate for an investment of £5000

Simple interest is paid only on the original investment, so it is the same every year. Compound interest increases because it is calculated on the original investment plus interest paid on previous years.

(a) for 2 years

You will need brilliant problem-solving skills to succeed in GCSE – **get practising now!**

....

(b) for 5 years.

....

3 Which is faster, 45 m/s or 165 km/h?
You must show your working.

Convert one of the speeds (either m/s into km/h or km/h into m/s) so they are in the same units.

$\times 60 \times 60 \div 1000$ m/s $\div 60 \div 60 \times 1000$

km/h

You will need brilliant problem-solving skills to succeed in GCSE – **get practising now!**

.... is faster because ....

4 Which has the greater density, a 45 cm³ piece of wood weighing 150 g or a 0.5 m³ piece of metal weighing 1240 kg?

$D = \dfrac{M}{V}$

To compare densities, they need to be in the same units, either g/cm³ or kg/m³.

....

Perimeter and area

1 (a) Work out the area of this right-angled triangle.

Area of a triangle = $\frac{1}{2}$ × base × height

   = $\frac{1}{2}$ × .... × ....

   = ... cm²

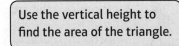

Use the vertical height to find the area of the triangle.

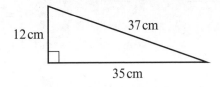

   (b) Work out the perimeter of the triangle.

Perimeter = ...

   = ...cm

Perimeter is the distance around the outside of a shape.

2 The perimeter of this rectangle is 22 mm.

   (a) Work out the length of side x.

$x + 7 + x + 7$ = ...

$2x + 14$ = ...

$2x$ = ...

x = ...mm

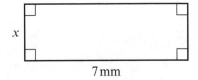

   (b) Work out the area of the rectangle.

..........................mm²

3 Work out the area of each shape.

   (a)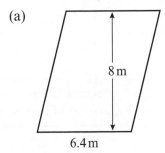

8 m

6.4 m

..........................m²

Area of a parallelogram = base × height

   (b)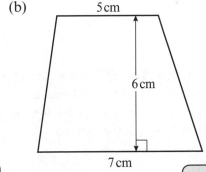

5 cm

6 cm

7 cm

..........................cm²

Area of a trapezium = $\frac{1}{2}$ × (a + b) × h where a and b are the parallel sides.

4 The area of this trapezium is 16 cm². Work out the height of the trapezium.

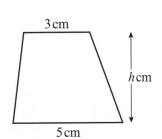

3 cm

h cm

5 cm

Substitute the values given into the formula for the area of a trapezium and then rearrange the equation and solve for h.

..........................cm

Compound shapes

Guided

1 Work out the area of this shape.

Area of rectangle A = ...

   = ...cm²

Area of rectangle B = ...

   = ...cm²

Area of shape = ...cm²

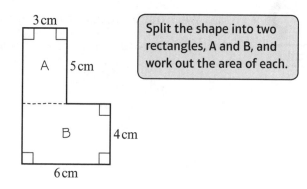

Split the shape into two rectangles, A and B, and work out the area of each.

2 Work out the area of this shape.

First find the length of the side labelled *x*.

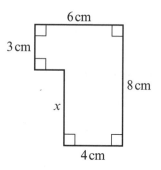

..............................cm²

3 The diagram shows a car park.

(a) Work out the area of the car park.

Split the shape into a rectangle and a triangle. Find the height of the triangle and use this to find the area of the triangle using the formula area = $\frac{1}{2} \times b \times h$

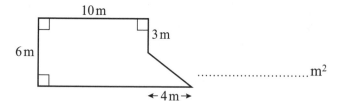

..........................m²

(b) A kerb will be laid around the outside of the car park, except for a 4-metre gap allowing vehicles to enter and leave the car park. How long will the kerb be?

Use Pythagoras' theorem to work out the hypotenuse of the triangle.

..........................m

4 A rhombus is cut out of a piece of card. What is the area of the remaining card?

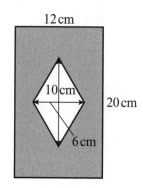

..........................cm²

Use subtraction to work out the area of the remaining card.
Area of card = area of rectangle − area of rhombus
Think of a way to subdivide the rhombus into smaller shapes.

Circles

Guided

1   Calculate the circumference of this circle.
    Give your answer to 1 decimal place.

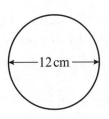

12 cm

A scientific calculator will have a button for π. You might need to press the SHIFT key first.

Circumference = πd

= $\pi \times$ ....

= ....cm (1 d.p)

2   A bicycle wheel has a radius of 30 cm.
    Work out the circumference of the wheel.

Which version of the formula for circumference do you need?

.... cm

3   Work out the area of each circle. Give your answers to 1 decimal place.

You need the radius to work out the area of a circle.

(a)

12 cm

Area of a circle = πr^2

(b)

30 cm

...........................cm^2

...........................cm^2

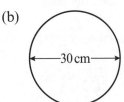

4   Work out the area of this circle.
    Leave your answer in terms of π.

10 cm

The answer will be ...π cm^2

...........................cm^2

5   A circle has a circumference of 20 cm.

(a) Calculate the diameter of the circle. Give your answer to 1 decimal place.

.... cm

(b) What is the radius of the circle (to 1 d.p.)?   .... cm

(c) Calculate the area of the circle (to 1 d.p.).

.... cm^2

63

Sectors of circles

Guided

1 Work out the area of this sector.
   Give your answer to 1 decimal place.

Area of a sector $= \dfrac{\theta}{360} \times \pi r^2$

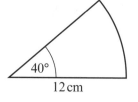

30°
5 cm

> Only round your numbers at the end of the calculation.

$\quad = \dfrac{.............}{360} \times \pi \times ....^2$

$\quad = \dfrac{.............}{.............} \times \pi \times ....$

$\quad = ... = ...\text{cm}^2$ (1 d.p.)

2 Work out the area of this sector. Give your answer to 2 decimal places.

40°
12 cm

.... cm²

Guided

PROBLEM SOLVED!

3 The diagram shows the sector of a
   circle with radius 15 cm.
   Work out the perimeter of the sector.

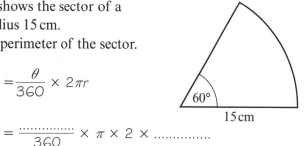

60°
15 cm

> Remember to include the two radii when finding the perimeter.

You will need brilliant problem-solving skills to succeed in GCSE – **get practising now!**

Length of arc $= \dfrac{\theta}{360} \times 2\pi r$

$\quad = \dfrac{.............}{360} \times \pi \times 2 \times ....$

$\quad = ... = ...\text{cm}$ (1 d.p.)

Perimeter = ... + ... + ... = ...cm (1 d.p.)

4 A circle has radius 9 m. A sector of the circle has angle 120°.
   Work out the perimeter of the sector.

> Work out what fraction of a whole circle the sector is.

.... m

PROBLEM SOLVED!

5 Which shape has the greater area?

> Work out the areas of the sectors then compare them.

You will need brilliant problem-solving skills to succeed in GCSE – **get practising now!**

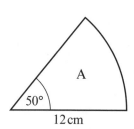

A
50°
12 cm

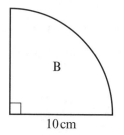

B
10 cm

....

Circles problem-solving

1 The diagram shows a quarter circle inside a square.
The length of each side of the square is 5 cm.

(a) Work out the area of the shaded shape.
Give your answer to 1 decimal place.

Area of square = ... × .... = ...cm²

Area of quarter circle = $\frac{1}{4}(\pi \times r^2)$

$= \frac{1}{4} \times \pi \times$ ....² = ...

= ....cm² (1 d.p.)

Shaded area = area of square − area of quarter circle

= .... − ....

= ....cm² (1 d.p.)

(b) Work out the percentage of the square that is shaded.
Give your answer to the nearest per cent.

Percentage shaded = $\dfrac{\text{shaded area}}{\text{area of square}} \times 100$

$= \dfrac{..............}{..............} \times 100$

= ....%

(c) Work out the perimeter of the shaded area.

> Write down your calculated answers to at least 4 d.p., and only round at the very end of a question.

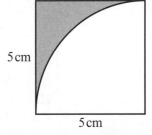

5 cm

5 cm

> You will need brilliant problem-solving skills to succeed in GCSE – **get practising now!**

.... cm

2 This shape is made from sectors of two circles, both with centre O.
Work out the shaded area of the shape.
Give your answer to 3 significant figures.

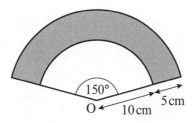

150°

O 10 cm 5 cm

> First, work out the radius of the larger sector. Subtract the area of the smaller sector from the area of the larger sector.

...........................cm² (3 s.f.)

3 Work out the perimeter of the shaded shape.
Give your answer in terms of π.

> You will need brilliant problem-solving skills to succeed in GCSE – **get practising now!**

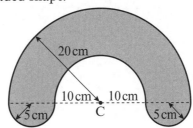

20 cm

10 cm 10 cm

5 cm C 5 cm

...........................cm

Plans and elevations

1 The diagram shows a 3D shape. On the grid draw the plan view and the front and side elevations of the shape.

Shade what you will see from each view first. This will help you imagine the 2D shape.

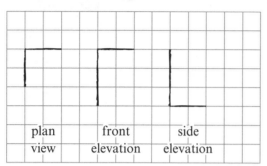

plan view   front elevation   side elevation

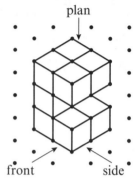

plan

front   side

2 The diagram shows a solid 3D shape. On the grid draw a plan view and front and side elevations of the shape.

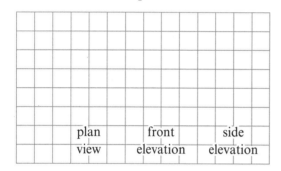

plan view   front elevation   side elevation

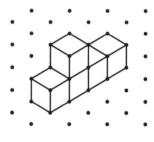

3 Here are the plan view, front elevation and side elevation of a 3D shape made from cubes. Draw the 3D shape on the isometric paper.

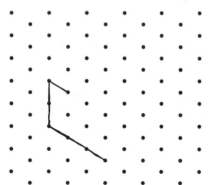

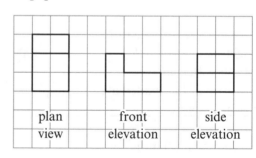

plan view   front elevation   side elevation

4 Here are the plan view. front elevation and side elevation of a 3D shape made from cubes. Draw the 3D shape on the isometric paper.

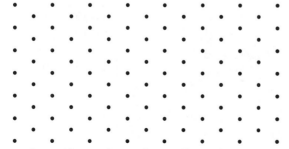

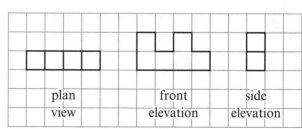

plan view   front elevation   side elevation

Surface area

1 Find the total surface area of this cuboid.

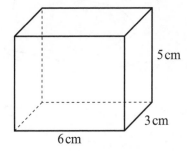

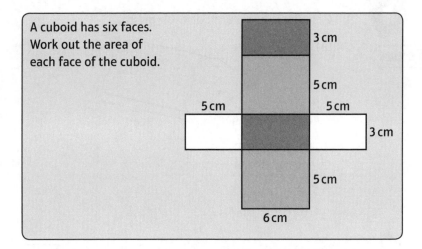

A cuboid has six faces. Work out the area of each face of the cuboid.

.... cm²

2 Find the total surface area of this triangular prism.

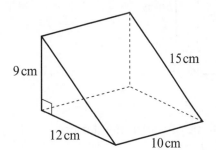

Work out the area of each face separately, then add them to find the total. If it helps, sketch each face to make sure you've got them all and have used the correct dimensions.

You will need brilliant problem-solving skills to succeed in GCSE – **get practising now!**

Area of left triangular face

= ½ × .... × .... = ... cm²

Area of right triangular face

= ½ × .... × .... = ... cm²

Area of bottom face = 12 × .... = ... cm²

Area of back face = 9 × .... = ... cm²

Area of slanted face = 15 × .... = ... cm²

Total surface area

= .... + ... + ... + ... + ... = ... cm²

3 Find the total surface area of this L-shaped prism.

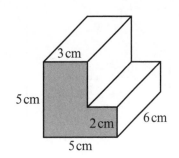

The front face is an L-shape. Find the area of the L-shape. Make sure you find the area of each face of the prism.

.... cm²

Had a go ☐   Nearly there ☐   Nailed it! ☐

Volume

Guided

1 Calculate the volume of each prism.

(a)

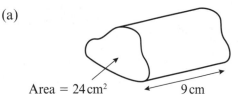

Area = 24 cm²   9 cm

Volume of prism
= area of cross-section × length

= 24 × ....

= ....cm³

(b)

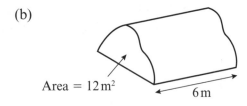

Area = 12 m²   6 m

Volume = ... × ....

= ....m³

2 Calculate the volume of this cuboid.

6 mm

3 mm

5 mm

A cuboid is a special type of prism whose volume can be calculated by multiplying length × width × height.

...........................mm³

3 Work out the volume of this triangular prism.

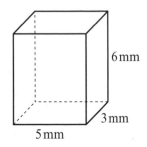

4 cm   5 cm

3 cm   6 cm

Area of a triangle = ½ × base × height

...........................cm³

4 Work out the volume of this L-shaped prism.

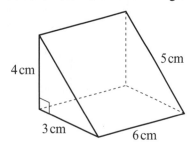

2 cm

5 cm

3 cm

8 cm

10 cm

7 cm

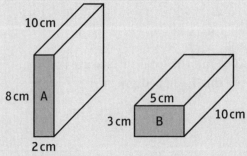
You could split the shape into two cuboids and work out the volume of each.

10 cm

8 cm A

2 cm

5 cm

3 cm B 10 cm

Or you could work out the area of the cross-section and multiply this by the length.

...........................cm³

Cylinders

1 The diagram shows a cylinder.

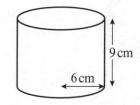

> **Guided**

(a) Calculate the volume of the cylinder.
Give your answer to 1 decimal place.

Volume = area of cross-section × height

$= \pi \times \text{................}^2 \times \text{................}$

$= \text{............................} = \text{................} \text{cm}^3$ (1 d.p.)

(b) Calculate the surface area of the cylinder.
Give your answer to 1 decimal place.

Area of a circle $= \pi r^2$

Surface area $= 2\pi rh + 2\pi r^2$

$= 2 \times \pi \times \text{................} \times \text{................} + 2 \times \pi \times \text{................}^2$

$= \text{............................} + \text{............................}$

$= \text{............................} = \text{................} \text{cm}^2$ (1 d.p.)

2 The diagram shows a cylinder.

First work out the radius of the cylinder.

(a) Work out the volume of the cylinder.
Give your answer to 3 significant figures.

.... m³ (3 s.f.)

(b) Work out the surface area of the cylinder. Give your answer to 3 significant figures.

.... m² (3 s.f.)

3 A wooden cylinder has a diameter of 9 cm.
A cylindrical core with a diameter of 5 cm
is drilled from the middle of the wooden
cylinder.
Work out the volume of wood that is left.
Give your answer to 1 decimal place.

Volume of wood remaining
= volume of large cylinder – volume of small cylinder

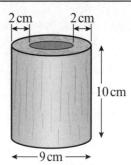

.... cm³ (1 d.p.)

Angle facts

Guided

1 AB is a straight line. Work out the size of angle x. Give a reason for each step of your working.

> **Remember:**
> • angles on a straight line add up to 180°
> • angles in a triangle add up to 180°.

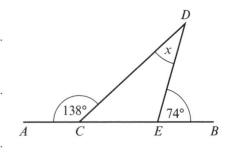

Angle $DCE = 180 -$ .... $=$ ....°

Reason: ....

Angle $DEC = 180 -$ .... $=$ ....°

Reason: ....

Angle $x = 180 - ($.............. $+$ ....$) =$ ....°

Reason: ....

2 Find the size of each missing angle on these parallel lines. Give reasons for your answers.

> **Choose from:**
> • co-interior angles add up to 180°
> • corresponding angles are equal
> • alternate angles are equal.

(a)

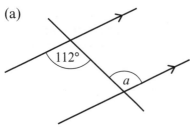

$a =$ ....°

....

(b)

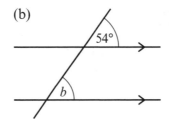

$b =$ ....°

....

(c)

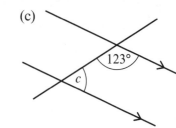

$c =$ ....°

....

3 Work out the size of the largest angle in this quadrilateral.

> Angles in a quadrilateral add up to 360°.

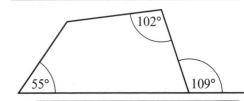

.........................°

4 A pair of parallel lines cross a triangle as shown.

(a) Work out the size of the angle labelled a. Give a reason for every step of your answer.

> Work out the size of angle RQS first.

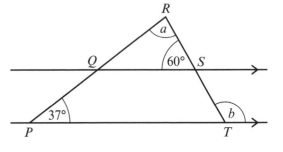

$a =$ ....°

Reasons: ....

....

(b) Work out the size of the angle labelled b. Give a reason for every step of your answer.

$b =$ ....°   Reasons: ....

Angles in parallelograms

Guided

1 *STUV* is a parallelogram. Work out the size of angle *RST*.
Give reasons for your answer.

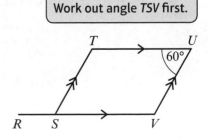

Work out angle *TSV* first.

Angle *TSV* = ...°

(opposite angles of a parallelogram are ....)

Angle *RST* = ...°

(angles on a straight line add up to ....°)

2 *ABCD* is a parallelogram. *ABE* is an isosceles triangle.
Work out the size of angle *x*.
Give reasons for your answer.

Use a range of angle facts.

x = ...°

3 *EFGH* is a parallelogram.
Work out the sizes of the angles labelled *x* and *y*.
Give reasons for your answers.

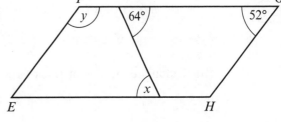

x = ...°

....

y = ...°

....

PROBLEM SOLVED!

4 *ABCD* is a parallelogram.

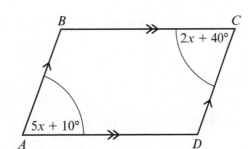

You will need brilliant problem-solving skills to succeed in GCSE – **get practising now!**

(a) Work out the size of angle *BCD*. State any angle facts you use.

Angle *BCD* = ...°

(b) Work out the size of angle *ABC*. State any angle facts you use.

Angle *ABC* = ...°

71

Angles in polygons

1 Work out the sum of the interior angles of an octagon.

> **Guided**

Sum of interior angles = $(n - 2) \times 180$

= $(\ldots\ldots\ldots - 2) \times 180$

= $\ldots\ldots\ldots \times 180 = \ldots\ldots\ldots°$

> An octagon has 8 sides.

2 The sum of the interior angles of a polygon is 720°.

(a) How many sides does the polygon have?

> Use the formula for the sum of the interior angles and rearrange to make n the subject.

$\ldots\ldots\ldots$ sides

(b) What is the name of the polygon? ....

3 (a) Work out the size of an exterior angle of a regular 12-sided polygon.

> **Guided**

Exterior angles of a polygon add up to $\ldots\ldots\ldots°$

Exterior angle of a regular 12-sided polygon = $\dfrac{\ldots\ldots\ldots}{12}$ = $\ldots\ldots\ldots°$

(b) Calculate the size of one of the interior angles.

Interior angle + exterior angle = 180°

Interior angle = $180 - \ldots\ldots\ldots = \ldots\ldots\ldots°$

4 (a) Work out the size of an exterior angle of a regular hexagon.

$\ldots\ldots\ldots°$

(b) Calculate the size of one of the interior angles.

$\ldots\ldots\ldots°$

5 Work out the size of one of the interior angles of a regular 18-sided polygon.

$\ldots\ldots\ldots°$

Angles problem-solving

1 Find the size of the angle labelled *a*.

> **Guided**

You need to find out the sum of the interior angles in a hexagon.

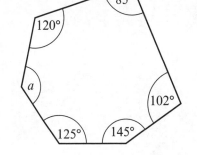

Sum of interior angles = $(n - 2) \times 180$

$\qquad = (\text{.............} - 2) \times 180$

$\qquad = \text{.............} \times 180 = \text{.............}°$

$a + \text{.............} + \text{.............} + \text{.............} + \text{.............} + \text{.............} = \text{.............}$

$a = \text{.............} - \text{.............} = \text{.............}°$

PROBLEM SOLVED!

2 The diagram shows three regular pentagons. Calculate the size of the angle labelled *x*.

Work out the size of one of the interior angles, *i*, of a regular pentagon using the rule
$$i = \frac{(n - 2) \times 180}{n}$$

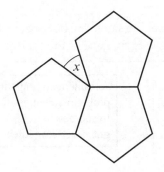

You will need brilliant problem-solving skills to succeed in GCSE – **get practising now!**

$x = \text{............................}°$

3 The diagram shows a regular heptagon and two squares. Work out the size of the angle labelled *y*. Give your answer to 1 decimal place.

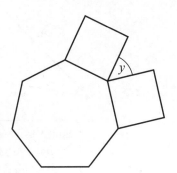

$y = \text{............................}°$

Pythagoras' theorem

Guided

1 *ABC* is a right-angled triangle.
Work out the length of the side labelled x.
Give your answer to 1 decimal place.

Label the longest side c and the other sides a and b. Then substitute your values into the formula for Pythagoras' theorem.

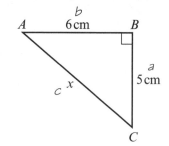

$c^2 = a^2 + b^2$

$x^2 = 5^2 + \ldots\ldots\ldots\ldots^2$

$x^2 = \ldots\ldots\ldots\ldots$

$x = \sqrt{\ldots\ldots\ldots\ldots}$

$\quad = \ldots\ldots\ldots\ldots\ldots\ldots\ldots$

$x = \ldots\ldots\ldots\ldots$ cm (1 d.p.)

2 *STU* is a right-angled triangle.
Work out the length of the side labelled y.
Give your answer to 1 decimal place.

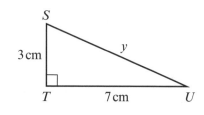

$y = \ldots\ldots\ldots\ldots\ldots\ldots\ldots$ cm

Guided

PROBLEM SOLVED!

3 The top of a vertical flagpole is tied by a 10 m rope to a point on the ground 4 m from the base of the flagpole.
What height is the flagpole?
Give your answer to 1 decimal place.

Draw a diagram and label the sides. You have been given the hypotenuse and you need to find one of the shorter sides.

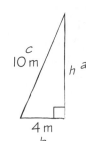

You will need brilliant problem-solving skills to succeed in GCSE – **get practising now!**

$c^2 = a^2 + b^2$

$h^2 = 10^2 - \ldots\ldots\ldots\ldots^2$

$h^2 = \ldots\ldots\ldots\ldots$

$h = \sqrt{\ldots\ldots\ldots\ldots}$

$\quad = \ldots\ldots\ldots\ldots\ldots\ldots\ldots$

$h = \ldots\ldots\ldots\ldots$ m (1 d.p.)

4 Work out the length of the side labelled p in this right-angled triangle.
Give your answer to 1 decimal place.

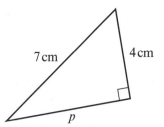

$p = \ldots\ldots\ldots\ldots\ldots\ldots\ldots$ cm

5 Work out the height of this isosceles triangle.
Give your answer to 1 decimal place.

Split the isosceles triangle into two right-angled triangles.

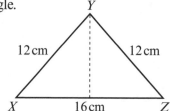

Height = $\ldots\ldots\ldots\ldots\ldots\ldots\ldots$ cm

Trigonometry 1

Guided

1 Each triangle has an angle highlighted.
Use this to label the hypotenuse and the opposite and adjacent sides of each triangle.

(a)
hyp
adj

(b)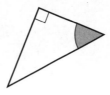

(c)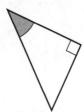

Guided

2 Calculate the size of the angle marked x.
Give your answer correct to 1 decimal place.

> Label the sides first to help you decide which trig ratio to choose.

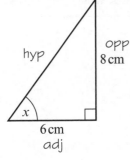

hyp   opp
8 cm

x

6 cm
adj

$$\tan x = \frac{\text{opposite}}{\text{adjacent}}$$

$$= \frac{8}{6}$$

$$x = \tan^{-1}\left(\frac{8}{6}\right)$$

> You need to use the tan⁻¹ function. Use the SHIFT or equivalent button on your calculator.

$$= \text{.............................} = \text{...............}° \text{ (1 d.p.)}$$

3 Calculate the size of the angle labelled y
in this right-angled triangle.
Give your answer to 1 decimal place.

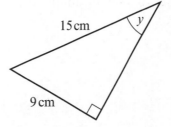

15 cm y

9 cm

> Label the sides of the triangle. Decide which ratio you are going to use from $S^O_H\ C^A_H\ T^O_A$.

$$y = \text{.............................}°$$

4 Calculate the size of the angle labelled z
in this isosceles triangle.
Give your answer to 1 decimal place.

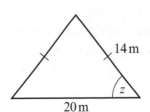

14 m

z

20 m

> Look for a right-angled triangle in the shape.

$$z = \text{.............................}°$$

Trigonometry 2

Guided

1 Calculate the length of the side marked x.
Give your answer to 1 decimal place.

> Label the sides to help you decide which trig ratio to use.

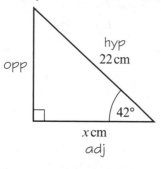

$$\cos \theta = \frac{\text{adjacent}}{\text{hypotenuse}}$$

$$\cos 42° = \frac{x}{\text{................}}$$

$x = \text{................} × \cos 42°$

$= \text{................................} = \text{................} \text{cm (1 d.p.)}$

2 Calculate the length of the side marked y.
Give your answer to 1 decimal place.

> Label the sides. Which trig ratio will you use?

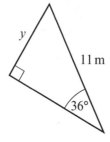

$y = \text{................................} \text{m}$

3 Calculate the length of the side marked p.
Give your answer to 3 significant figures.

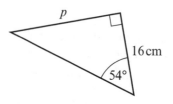

$p = \text{................................} \text{cm (3 s.f.)}$

4 Calculate the length of the side marked b.
Give your answer to 1 decimal place.

> Rearrange the formula to find b.

$b = \text{................................} \text{mm (1 d.p.)}$

Problem-solving with triangles

1 Meryl drives 100 km east from Amberside to Bellwick. From Bellwick she drives 80 km north to Clipton before returning directly to Amberside.

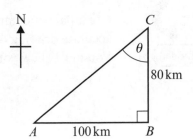

(a) How far has Meryl driven altogether? Give your answer to the nearest km.

First use Pythagoras' theorem to find the distance from Amberside to Clipton.

$(AC)^2 = (AB)^2 + (BC)^2$

$= 10\,000 + \dots\dots\dots$

$AC = \sqrt{\dots\dots\dots} = \dots\dots\dots\text{km}$

Total distance $= \dots\dots\dots + \dots\dots\dots + \dots\dots\dots = \dots\dots\dots\text{km}$

(b) What is the size of the angle labelled θ? Give your answer to 2 decimal places.

Use trigonometry – label the sides of the triangle to help you decide which trig ratio to use.

$\theta = \dots\dots\dots\dots\dots°$

2 Find the size of the angle labelled θ in this diagram. Give your answer to the nearest whole number.

Use Pythagoras' theorem to work out BD, which is the hypotenuse of triangle BCD. Then use trigonometry to find the angle labelled θ.

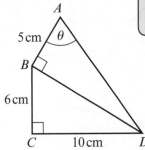

You will need brilliant problem-solving skills to succeed in GCSE – **get practising now!**

$\theta = \dots\dots\dots\dots\dots°$

3 The diagram shows two right-angled triangles.

(a) Calculate the length of BC to 2 decimal places.

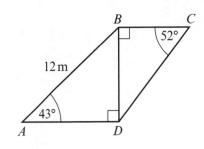

$BC = \dots\dots\dots\dots\dots\text{m (2 d.p.)}$

(b) Calculate the area of triangle BCD. Give your answer to the nearest m².

$Area = \dots\dots\dots\dots\dots\text{m}^2$

Constructions 1

1 Use a pair of compasses and a ruler to construct an accurate drawing of triangle *PQR*.
You must show your construction arcs.

> Guided

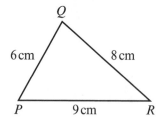

Open your compasses to 6 cm to draw an arc centred on *P*.

P ————————————————————— R

2 (a) Use a ruler and a pair of compasses to construct the perpendicular bisector of the line *AB*.

Open your compasses to more than 5 cm. Draw an arc centred on *A*. Keep your compasses at the same radius and draw another arc centred on *B*. Draw a line between the two points where the arcs cross.

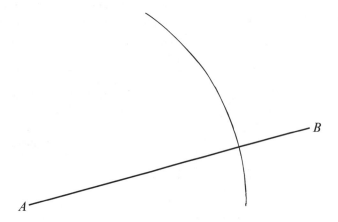

(b) Use a ruler to check that your line bisects line *AB* and use a protractor to check that the angle between the lines is a right angle.

(c) Mark a point × on your perpendicular bisector.
Check that it is the same distance from *A* and *B*.

Constructions 2

1   Use a ruler and a pair of compasses to bisect this angle.

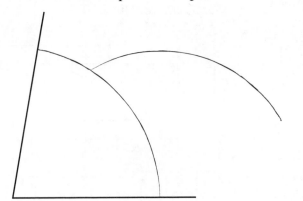

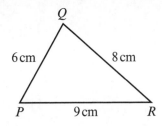

> Remember to leave in your arcs to show that you have used compasses.

2   Use a ruler and a pair of compasses to construct an angle of 45°.

> Construct the perpendicular bisector of this line. This will give you a right angle. Then construct the angle bisector of one of your right angles.

A ——————————————— B

3   (a)   Use a ruler and a pair of compasses to bisect one of the angles of this equilateral triangle.

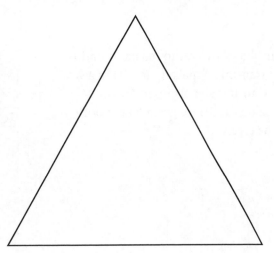

   (b)   Use a protractor to check that the bisected angle is 30°.

79

Loci

Guided

1 (a) Draw the locus of all the points that are 3 cm from the point O.

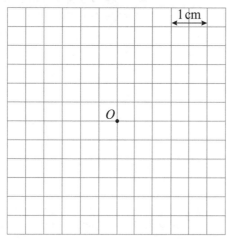

(b) Draw the locus of all points that are 2 cm from line AB.

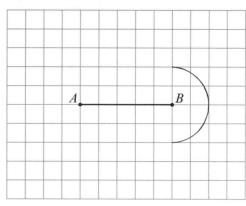

A locus is a set of points that satisfy a certain rule.

2 $ABCD$ is a rectangle drawn on cm^2 paper. Shade the region inside $ABCD$ that is closer to A than B and is less than 5 cm from C.

Draw a circle with radius 5 cm with centre C.

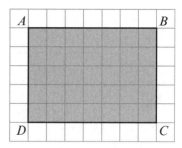

PROBLEM SOLVED!

3 The diagram shows two radio masts, A and B. Mast A can transmit signals up to 70 km away. Mast B can transmit signals up to 60 km. Shade the region on the diagram where both signals can be received.

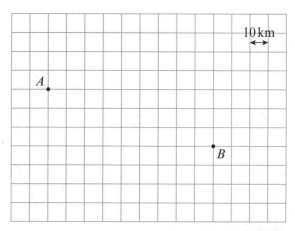

You will need brilliant problem-solving skills to succeed in GCSE – **get practising now!**

Transformations

1 Reflect the triangle in the line $y = 2$.

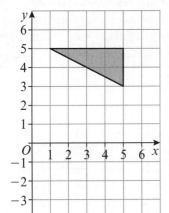

> The reflected shape should be the same distance away from the mirror line as the original shape.

2 (a) Describe fully the single transformation that maps shape S onto shape T.

> Use tracing paper to help you find the centre of rotation.

Rotation ....°

about (.............., ...)

> To fully describe a rotation, you need to specify 'rotation' and give the angle of rotation, the direction of rotation and the centre of rotation.

(b) Describe fully the transformation that will map shape S onto shape U.

....

....

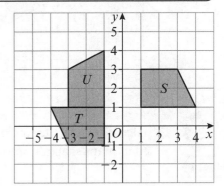

3 (a) Describe fully the single transformation that maps shape C onto shape D.

.... by the vector $\begin{pmatrix} ...... \\ ...... \end{pmatrix}$

> $\begin{pmatrix} a \\ b \end{pmatrix}$ is a translation vector that means a right and b up.

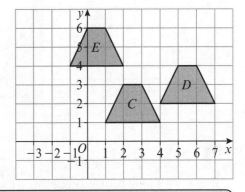

(b) Describe fully the single transformation that maps shape D onto shape E.

> To fully describe the translation you need to specify 'translation' and give the vector. Read the question carefully. You need to write the vector from shape D to shape E.

....

(c) Describe fully the single transformation that maps shape E onto shape D.

....

(d) Write down what you notice about your answers to parts (b) and (c).

....

Enlargement

1   On the grid, enlarge shape *A* by a scale factor of 2, centre of enlargement (0, 3).

> Check that the length of each side of the enlarged shape is twice the corresponding length of the original shape.

> Count the squares horizontally and vertically from the centre of enlargement to each vertex on the shape. Multiply each distance by 2 to find the corresponding vertex on the enlarged shape.

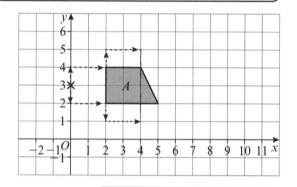

2   On the grid, enlarge shape *A* by a scale factor of $\frac{1}{2}$, centre of enlargement (0, 2).

> A scale factor between 0 and 1 will make the shape smaller.

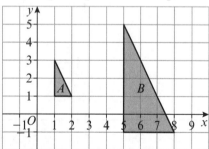

3   Describe fully the single transformation that maps shape *A* onto shape *B*.

> Scale factor = $\dfrac{\text{enlarged length}}{\text{original length}}$
>
> To find the centre of enlargement, draw lines through corresponding vertices of the object and image. These will meet at the centre of enlargement.

.... scale factor ...., centre of enlargement (..............., ...)

4   Describe fully the single transformation that maps shape *B* onto shape *C*.

> To fully describe an enlargement, you need to state that it is an enlargement, and give the scale factor and the centre of enlargement.

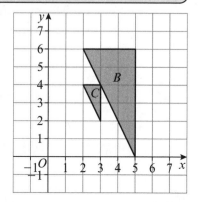

....

Combined transformations

1 (a) Reflect shape *A* in the *x*-axis. Label the image *B*.

Guided

(b) Reflect shape *B* in the *y*-axis. Label the image *C*.

(c) Describe fully the single transformation that maps shape *A* onto shape *C*.

...... rotation ....° about

centre (..............., ...)

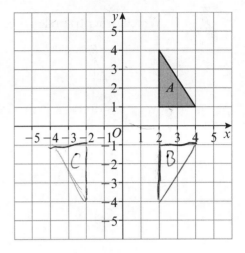

2 (a) Rotate shape *S* 180° about (0, 0). Label the image *T*.

(b) Reflect shape *T* in the *y*-axis. Label the image *V*.

(c) Describe fully the single transformation that maps shape *S* onto shape *V*.

....

Use tracing paper to help.

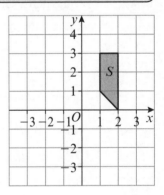

3 (a) Translate shape *P* by the vector $\begin{pmatrix} -3 \\ -4 \end{pmatrix}$.
Label the image *Q*.

(b) Translate shape *Q* by the vector $\begin{pmatrix} 5 \\ -3 \end{pmatrix}$.
Label the image *R*.

(c) Describe fully the single transformation that maps shape *P* onto shape *R*.

....

(d) Describe fully the single transformation that maps shape *R* onto shape *P*.

....

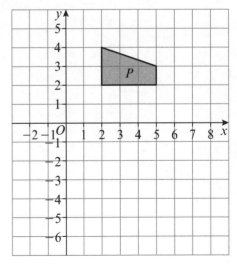

(e) What do you notice about your answers to parts (c) and (d)?

....

Congruent shapes

1   Which other triangle is congruent to triangle *ABC*? Give reasons for your answer.

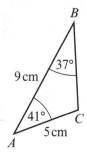 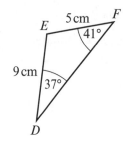 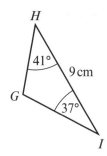

....

2   *ST* and *VU* are parallel lines. *ST* = *VU*.
    Show that triangles *STX* and *VUX* are
    congruent. Give your reasons.

Guided

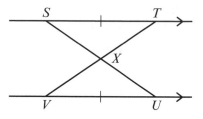

Angle *SXT* = angle *VXU* because   ....

....

Angle *VUS* = angle *TSU* because   ....

Angle *TVU* = angle *STV* because   ....

ST = *VU* (given)

So triangle .... is congruent to triangle ....

3   *ABCD* is a rectangle. Show that triangle *ABC*
    and triangle *CDA* are congruent.
    Give your reasons.

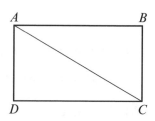

Similar triangles

1 Explain why triangles *A* and *B* are similar.

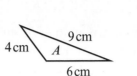

Look at the lengths of corresponding sides.

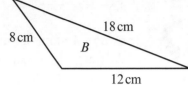

Guided

2 Triangles *C* and *D* are mathematically similar.

(a) Work out the length of the side marked *p*.

For part (a), find the scale factor (SF) from *C* to *D*, and for part (b) find the SF from *D* to *C*.

$SF = \dfrac{15}{6} = $ ....

$p = 8 \times SF = 8 \times$ ....

$= $ ....cm

(b) Work out the length of *q*.

$SF = \dfrac{6}{15} = $ ....

$q = 10 \times SF = 10 \times$ .... $= $ ....cm

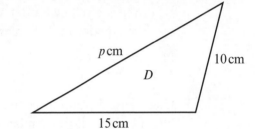

PROBLEM SOLVED!

3 Triangle *PQR* is similar to triangle *QST*. Work out the length of *PT*.

Use similar triangles to work out the length of *PQ* first.

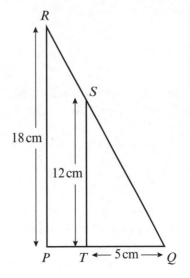

You will need brilliant problem-solving skills to succeed in GCSE – **get practising now!**

$PT = $ ....cm

Experimental probability

Guided

1 The probability that a biased dice will land on a 3 is 0.5. Sam rolls the dice 200 times. Work out an estimate for the number of times the dice will land on a 3.

Estimate for number of 3s = ... × 200 = ...

Guided

2 A box contains an unknown number of different coloured beads.
Jacqui picks a bead at random from the box, notes its colour and then replaces it.
She does this 30 times. The table shows her results.

Colour	Yellow	Blue	Green	Orange
Frequency	8	6	7	9

(a) What is the probability that the next bead Jacqui picks is orange?

P(orange) = $\frac{..........}{30}$

> Experimental probability = $\frac{\text{frequency of outcome}}{\text{total frequency}}$

(b) How many times would Jacqui expect to pick a yellow bead if she repeats the experiment 300 times?

> Expected outcome =
> number of trials × probability of successful outcome

P(yellow) = 300 × $\frac{..........}{..........}$ = ...

3 Chloe asks a group of people to memorise some words. She then records the number of words they can remember after 5 minutes.

Number of words	Frequency
4	2
5	8
6	12
7	10
8	8

(a) Work out the experimental probability of remembering 6 words.

> Work out the total number of people in the experiment.

....

(b) Chloe repeats the experiment with 200 people. Estimate the number of people who will remember 7 words.

> P(remembering 7 words) × 200

....

4 A bag contains 30 counters.
There are 8 green counters and 12 blue counters, and the rest are black.
Mike picks a counter at random and then replaces it. He does this 600 times.
Estimate the number of times Mike will pick a black counter.

....

Probability diagrams

1 Ewa spins a fair spinner numbered 1–5 and flips a coin.

(a) Complete this sample space diagram to show all the possible outcomes.

		Spinner				
		1	**2**	**3**	**4**	**5**
Coin	**H**	H 1			H 4	
	T		T 2			

(b) Work out the probability that Ewa spins an even number and flips tails.

Probability (even, tails) = ... / ......

> First work out the total number of possible outcomes.

2 Corrinne did a survey to find the number of pets owned by her friends.
5 friends had a dog and a cat.
13 friends had a dog.
11 friends had a cat.
1 friend had no pet.

> Always start with the intersection. Subtract this number to work out the numbers for other sections.

(a) Complete the Venn diagram to show this information.

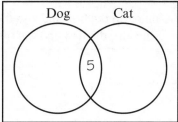

(b) Work out the probability that one of her friends only had a dog.

> How many people did Corrinne ask?

3 45 adults and children were asked if they preferred the cinema or the theatre.
10 adults said they preferred the cinema.
5 of the 17 people who preferred the theatre were children.

> Use the information given in the question to fill in parts of the table. Then use addition or subtraction to complete the rest of the table.

(a) Complete this two-way table.

	Cinema	Theatre	Total
Adults			
Children			
Total			

(b) What is the probability that a person chosen at random preferred the cinema?

Probability tree diagrams

1 Duncan plays chess. He can either win a game or not win a game.
   The probability that Duncan wins a game is 0.7.

   (a) What is the probability that Duncan does **not** win a game?

   P(does not win) = 1 − P(wins) = 1 − .... = ...

   (b) Duncan plays two games of chess.
        Complete this probability tree diagram to show the probabilities.

> The probabilities on each pair of branches must add up to 1.

	1st game	2nd game	Outcome	Probability

                                    0.7 ⟋ Wins   WW   0.7 × 0.7 = 0.49
                              Wins ⟨
                        0.7 ⟋   .... ⟍ Does   ....
                                                 not win
                    ⟨
                        .... ⟍   .... ⟋ Wins   ....
                                 Does ⟨
                                 not win .... ⟍ Does   ....
                                                    not win

   (c) What is the probability that Duncan loses both games?   ....

   (d) Work out the probability that Duncan
        wins one game and loses the other.

> He could win the first and lose the second or he could lose the first and win the second.

   0.7 × .... + 0.3 × .... = ... + ... = ...

2 The probability that Lara passes her driving test is $\frac{4}{5}$.
   The probability that Clara passes the test is $\frac{1}{2}$.

   (a) What is the probability that Lara fails the test?   ....

   (b) Complete the tree diagram to show this information.

	Lara	Clara	Outcome	Probability

                              $\frac{1}{2}$ ⟋ Pass   ....
                        Pass ⟨
                  $\frac{4}{5}$ ⟋   .... ⟍ Fail   ....
                ⟨
                  .... ⟍   .... ⟋ Pass   ....
                           Fail ⟨
                                  .... ⟍ Fail   ....

   (c) What is the probability that both Lara and Clara pass the driving test?

> Multiply as you go along the branches.

                                                                    ....

   (d) What is the probability that only one of them passes the driving test?

                                                                    ....

Mutually exclusive and independent events

1   Kim spins a fair spinner numbered 1–8 once.
Which of these events are mutually exclusive? Give your reasons.

(a) Spinning a 3 and a 7

Mutually exclusive because ....

(b) Spinning an even number and a multiple of 3

....

(c) Spinning an even number and an odd number

....

(d) Spinning a factor of 6 and a factor of 8

....

2   Which of these events are independent? Give your reasons.

(a) From a pencil case that contains red and green pens, lending a green pen to your
friend and then picking another green pen at random.

....

(b) Spinning a 2 on a spinner and
getting heads when flipping a coin.

> When events are independent, the probability of the first event does not affect the probability of the second event.

....

3   Susan rolls a fair 1–6 dice once.
What is the probability of getting a 2 or a 5?

> For mutually exclusive events P(A or B) = P(A) + P(B)

....

4   The probability that James wins a game of tennis is 0.8.
James plays two games of tennis.
What is the probability that he wins both games?

> For independent events
> P(A and B) = P(A) × P(B)

....

5   Juan rolls a fair 1–6 dice three times.
What is the probability of getting a 4 all three times?

....

Averages and range

Guided

1 Here are 10 numbers: 4   5   12   1   5   3   4   10   5   1

(a) Write down the mode.

> The mode is the most common value.

The mode is ....

(b) Work out the mean.

Mean = $\dfrac{4 + 5 + 12 + 1 + 5 + 3 + 4 + 10 + 5 + 1}{10}$ = $\dfrac{..........}{10}$ = ...

(c) Work out the median.

> Write the numbers in order. Cross off the smallest and largest values in pairs. When there are two middle numbers, the median is halfway between these numbers.

~~1~~   ~~1~~   3   4   4   5   5   5   ~~10~~   ~~12~~

Median = $\dfrac{.......... + ...}{2}$ = ...

(d) Work out the range.

> Range = largest value – smallest value

Range = ... – .... = ...

2 These are the marks out of 100 that Jenny received in 10 maths tests.

88   80   88   20   76   78   88   85   83   85

(a) Work out the mode, median and mean of Jenny's marks.

Mode: ....   Median: ....   Mean: ....

(b) Which is the best average to use?
Give reasons for your answer.

> Consider how the mark of 20 affects each average.

....

....

PROBLEM SOLVED!

3 (a) Here are three different number cards.

> You will need brilliant problem-solving skills to succeed in GCSE – **get practising now!**

The median of these cards is 4. The range of these cards is 5.
Work out the missing two numbers on the cards.

....

Averages from tables

Guided

1 The table shows the number of points scored by 20 students in a competition.

Number of points x	Frequency f	$x \times f$
0	1	$0 \times 1 =$ ....
1	3	$1 \times 3 =$ ....
2	8	.... $\times$ .... $=$ ....
3	5	.... $\times$ .... $=$ ....
4	3	.... $\times$ .... $=$ ....

(a) Write down the mode.

Mode = ... points

(b) Work out the mean number of points scored.

> Work out the total number of points by calculating number of points × frequency ($x \times f$). If this column is not given, add the column onto the table.

Mean = $\dfrac{\text{total number of points}}{\text{total frequency}}$ = $\dfrac{..........}{..........}$ = ... points

Guided

2 The table shows the ages of people at a tennis club. Work out an estimate of the mean age.

> The midpoint of a group is a good estimate when you don't have exact values. Add a column to find the midpoint, x. Then add a column for $f \times x$ to work out the total of all the ages.

Age, a (years)	Frequency f	Midpoint x	$f \times x$
$20 < a \leqslant 30$	5	25	$5 \times 25 = 125$
$30 < a \leqslant 40$	10	....	.... $\times$ .... $=$ ....
$40 < a \leqslant 50$	4	....	.... $\times$ .... $=$ ....
$50 < a \leqslant 60$	6	....	.... $\times$ .... $=$ ....

Mean = $\dfrac{\text{total } f \times x}{\text{total } f}$ = $\dfrac{..........}{..........}$ = ... years

3 The table shows the total amount A (in pounds, £) spent on clothes by a group of people in one month.

Amount spent on clothes, A (£)	Frequency
$0 < A \leqslant 40$	4
$40 < A \leqslant 80$	12
$80 < A \leqslant 120$	21
$120 < A \leqslant 160$	3

Work out an estimate of the mean amount spent.

£............................

Two-way tables

1 This two-way table gives some information about the pets owned by students in Years 7 and 8.

> Use addition or subtraction to work out the missing numbers, e.g. 10 + ? = 23, 23 + 21 + ? = 60

(a) Complete the two-way table.

	Cat	Dog	Other	Total
Year 7	10			30
Year 8			5	30
Total	23	21		60

(b) How many Year 8 children own a dog?

.... children

2 This two-way table shows some information about which attraction adults and children liked best.

	Museum	Art gallery	Zoo	Total
Adults	9			31
Children	15	8		
Total			28	70

(a) Complete the two-way table.

(b) How many children liked the zoo best?

.... children

> **Guided**
>
> **PROBLEM SOLVED!**

3 A café recorded how many hot and cold drinks were bought by adults and children one day.
45 drinks were sold altogether.
12 adults bought a hot drink.
15 children bought a cold drink.
20 adults bought a drink.

> You will need brilliant problem-solving skills to succeed in GCSE – **get practising now!**

(a) Use this information to complete the two-way table.

	Hot drink	Cold drink	Total
Adults	12		....
Children		15	
Total			45

> Use the information given to fill in some numbers and then work out the missing numbers.

(b) How many children bought a hot drink?

.... children

4 60 students were asked how they travelled to school.
8 out of the 25 girls who were asked said they walked to school.
15 boys took the bus and 12 boys walked to school. 25 students altogether took the bus to school.
8 boys used another mode of transport. How many girls used another mode of transport?

> Draw a two-way table.

.... girls

Analysing data

1 Sara does a survey to find out if people in a tennis club like the facilities.
The tennis club has 1200 members.
Circle the most appropriate sample size for her survey.

> 10% of the population is a good sample size.

A   12   B   120   C   1200

2 A teacher wants to test the hypothesis: 'Students who complete their homework do better in maths tests'.
Which of these sets of data does the teacher need to collect?

A   Age of students

B   Homework record

C   Test scores

D   Gender of students

....

3 A student wants to find out the most popular football team.
He decides to ask his friends.
Explain why this is not a good sample to use.

....

4 Michael wants to do a survey to find out the most popular film genre in his school.
There are 700 people in his school.

(a)   How many students should he sample?

....

(b)   Which of these methods of collection would give a biased sample?

A   A random sample of students in his year

B   A random sample of boys

C   Asking his friends

D   A random sample of students in the school

....

(c)   Design a suitable data collection sheet for Michael to collect the information.

Interpreting charts

1   The pie chart shows some students' preferred method
of communication.
6 students use social media as their preferred method.

> Guided

PROBLEM SOLVED!

(a) How many students use texting as their
preferred method?

...............° represents 6 students

so ....° represents 1 student

Number of students who prefer texting

= ....° ÷ ....° = ...

(b) How many students were asked altogether?

360° ÷ .... = ...

┌───┐
│ 360° ÷ number of degrees for 1 person   │
└───┘

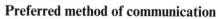
Preferred method of communication

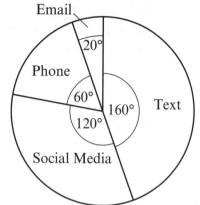

Email, 20°, Phone 60°, 160° Text, 120°, Social Media

┌─────────────────────────────┐
│ You will need brilliant   │
│ problem-solving skills   │
│ to succeed in GCSE –   │
│ **get practising now!**   │
└─────────────────────────────┘

2   The pie chart shows a football team's results for one season.
The team lost four matches.

(a) How many matches did they win?

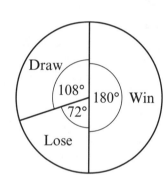

Draw 108°, 180° Win, 72°, Lose

.... matches

(b) How many matches did they play altogether?

.... matches

3   Pedro recorded the number of spam emails
his friends received in one week.
The stem and leaf diagram shows his results.

```
0 | 4 5 6
1 | 2 2 4 6 7 8
2 | 3 9 9 9
3 | 2 5
```

(a) Work out the range.

Key: 1 | 2 = 12 emails

....

(b) What is the mode?

....

(c) Work out the median.

┌─────────────────────────────────┐
│ The median is the middle value. │
└─────────────────────────────────┘

....

Misleading graphs and charts

1 The graph shows a sales representative's sales figures for two years. The sales representative says, 'I doubled my sales from 2014 to 2015.' Explain why he is incorrect and give one reason why this graph is misleading.

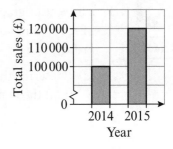

In 2014, the total sales were £..............................

In 2015, the total sales were £..............................

The sales have increased by £.........................., not £..........................

The graph is misleading because ....

2 The pie charts show the results of matches played by a hockey team in March and April.

> Pie charts show proportions.

The team manager says that they won more matches in April than in March. Explain why she could be incorrect.

....

3 The two graphs show the numbers of customers who bought goods from a website over four years.

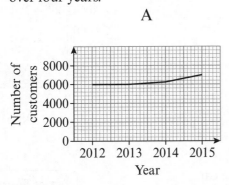

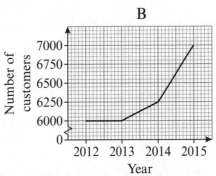

(a) The sales director says, 'Numbers of customers have increased dramatically over the last four years.' Which graph is she using? Explain your reasons.

....

(b) Why is the graph that she used misleading?

> Look at the axes on the graphs.

....

Scatter graphs

Guided

1 The scatter graph gives information about the number of ice creams sold and the temperature (°C) for 13 days in July.

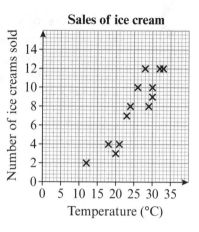

Sales of ice cream

(a) Describe the relationship between the temperature and the number of ice creams sold.

As the temperature increases the number of ice creams

sold ....

(b) What type of correlation does the scatter graph show?

> Choose from 'positive', 'negative' or 'no' correlation.

....

(c) Draw a line of best fit on the scatter graph.

> The line of best fit is a straight line that is as close to the points as possible. There should be equal numbers of points on both sides.

(d) On another day in July, the temperature was 25 °C. Use your line of best fit to estimate the number of ice creams sold that day.

....

2 The scatter graph gives information about the ages of some cars and their value (in £).

(a) Describe the relationship between the age of a car and its value.

....

....

(b) What type of correlation does the scatter graph show?

....

(c) A car is 7 years old. Estimate the value of the car.

> Draw a line of best fit.

£.............................

Frequency polygons

1 The table gives some information about the ages of 34 people in a choir.

Age, a (years)	Frequency
$10 < a \leq 20$	6
$20 < a \leq 30$	10
$30 < a \leq 40$	4
$40 < a \leq 50$	2
$50 < a \leq 60$	1

On the grid, draw a frequency polygon to show this information.

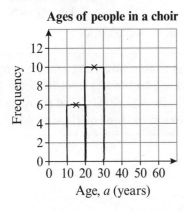

Ages of people in a choir

> Start by drawing a bar chart for the grouped data. Use this to mark the midpoints.

2 John carried out a survey of 20 students in Year 12.
He measured the length of their armspan in centimetres.
The table shows his results.

Length, x (cm)	Frequency
$140 < x \leq 150$	1
$150 < x \leq 160$	9
$160 < x \leq 170$	8
$170 < x \leq 180$	2

On the grid, draw a frequency polygon to show this information.

> To work out the midpoint of a group, add the boundary values together and divide by 2.

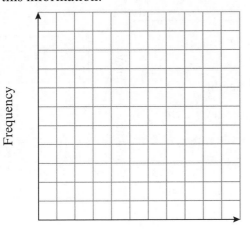

Length, x (cm)

Cumulative frequency

1 The cumulative frequency graph shows the amount of time 30 students spent doing their homework in one week.

Time (hours)	Cumulative frequency
$0 < t \leqslant 2$	2
$2 < t \leqslant 4$	6
$4 < t \leqslant 6$	18
$6 < t \leqslant 8$	26
$8 < t \leqslant 10$	30

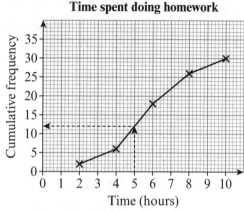

Time spent doing homework

(a) How many students spent fewer than 5 hours doing their homework? ....

(b) What was the median time spent doing homework?

> The median is the middle value. 30 students were asked so the median value will be the 30 ÷ 2 = 15th value. Go to 15 on the Cumulative frequency axis, read across to the graph line and then down to the time on the horizontal axis.

.... hours

(c) Use the graph to work out the interquartile range.

Interquartile range = upper quartile − lower quartile

= .... − .... = ... hours

2 The table shows the heights of 50 plants.

(a) Complete the column for Cumulative frequency.

> Work out the cumulative frequency by adding up the frequencies as you go along.

Height of plants, h (cm)	Frequency	Cumulative frequency
$0 < h \leqslant 10$	8	
$10 < h \leqslant 20$	10	
$20 < h \leqslant 30$	18	
$30 < h \leqslant 40$	10	
$40 < h \leqslant 50$	4	

(b) On the grid draw a cumulative frequency graph to show this information.

(c) Use your graph to work out the median height.

............................cm

(d) Use your graph to work out the interquartile range.

............................cm

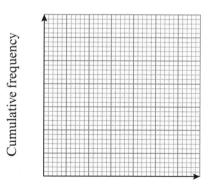

Height of plants, h (cm)

Box plots

1 Plants were grown in two different types of soil, A and B.
   The box plots show the heights of these plants after
   10 days.

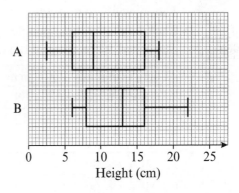

(a) Which soil produced the tallest plant?   ....

(b) Work out the interquartile range for soil A.

   ....cm

(c) Which soil was better for growing the plant? | Compare the median and the interquartile range. |
   Give reasons for your answer.

   ....

2 Students in Year 8 and Year 9 did a sponsored walk
   to raise money for charity.
   The box plot shows the amounts of money (in £)
   raised by the students in Year 8.

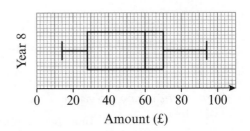

(a) What was the median amount of money raised by students in Year 8?   £...........................

(b) What was the interquartile range for Year 8 students?

   £...........................

Here is information about the amounts of money raised by students in Year 9.

Smallest amount	£18
Largest amount	£94
Median	£66
Lower quartile	£48
Upper quartile	£80

(c) On the grid, draw a box plot to show this information.

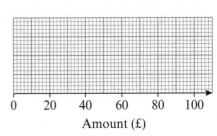

(d) Which year group performed better in the sponsored walk? Give reasons for your answer.

   ....

Writing a report

> **Guided**

Karen wants to find out how much time people spend shopping in her local supermarket.
She thinks that most people spend more than 30 minutes shopping.
She asked 50 people and the table shows her results.

Time, t (minutes)	Frequency, f
$0 < t \leqslant 10$	9
$10 < t \leqslant 20$	12
$20 < t \leqslant 30$	9
$30 < t \leqslant 40$	10
$40 < t \leqslant 50$	9
$50 < t \leqslant 60$	1

Write a report to test Karen's
hypothesis. Include averages
and a frequency polygon
in your report.

> Add another column to the table to calculate the midpoint, x.
>
> Add another column for $f \times x$. The estimated mean is $\dfrac{\text{total } f \times x}{\text{total } f}$

Averages and range

The estimated mean is .... minutes

The modal group is .... minutes

The median class interval is .... minutes

The estimated range = largest value − smallest value

$$= \text{..............} - \text{..............} = \text{..............} \text{ minutes}$$

Frequency polygon

> Plot the frequency at the midpoint of each class interval.

> In your conclusion, mention the statistics you have calculated. Mention any outliers and the effects they might have. Don't forget to comment on whether the data support the hypothesis, and include suggestions for improving the investigation.

Conclusion

....

....

....

....

....

To improve this investigation, Karen could ....

....

....

Answers

NUMBER

1. Multiplication and division
1. (a) 208 (b) 800 (c) 270 (d) 0.21
   (e) 4 (f) 16
2. (a) 4368 (b) 8820 (c) 13 838
3. 4500 apples
4. (a) 175 (b) 163 (c) 59.2 (d) 49.875
   (e) 54.$\dot{6}$
5. (a) 384 (b) 542

2. Decimals
1. (a) 4 (b) 3.8 (c) 3.83
2. (a) 6000 (b) 80 (c) 0.9
3. (a) 3800 (b) 0.37 (c) 0.0094
4. (a) 27 500 (b) 3 000 000 (c) 0.003 750
5. (a) $6 \times 4 = 24$
   (b) $\frac{7 \times 40}{80 \div 20} = \frac{280}{4} = 70$
6. 11 shirts

3. Using powers of 10
1.

Country	Population	Population
Albania	2 892 000	**2.892** million
Costa Rica	**4 870 000**	4.87 million
Barbados	285 000	**0.285** million
Brunei	**430 000**	0.430 million

2. (a) £3 250 000 (b) 0.1157 million
3. (a) 3958 (b) 9.376 (c) 38 000 (d) 0.52
   (e) 0.725 (f) 4790 (g) 0.8327 (h) 514 870
4. (a) 4.9 (b) 0.62 (c) 510 (d) 7900
5. ×1000

4. Calculating with decimals
1. (a) 815.04 (b) 17.28 (c) 10.53
2. (a) 8.53 (b) 56.2 (c) 45.3
3. £17.35
4. 12.4 cm
5. 13 bags
6. Any acceptable explanation such as: $30 \times 20 = 600$
   (rounding to 1 s.f.); $32.6 \times 17.4 = 567.24$

5. Negative numbers
1. (a) −3 (b) −4 (c) −6 (d) 10
2. (a) −18 (b) 35 (c) 90 (d) −6
   (e) 3 (f) −8 (g) 36 (h) −1
3. 7 °C
4. (a) 15 degrees (b) 28 degrees (c) 7 °C
5. (a) $-8 \times 5 = -40$ (b) $-8 \times 5 \times -3 = 120$

6. Place-value calculations
1. (a) Gina, Hetty, Ellie, Fiona
   (b) Darius, Brendan, Aaron, Caleb
2. −9.38, −9.399, −9.4, −9.44
3. (a) 252 (b) 2.52 (c) 72 (d) 3.5
4. (a) 2304 (b) 9216 (c) 960 (d) 0.48
5. Any acceptable explanation such as: $50 \div 10 = 5$ (rounding
   to 1 s.f.); $54.32 \div 9.7 = 5.6$

7. Complex operations
1. (a) $(8 - 4) + 2 = 6$ or $(8 + 4) \div 2 = 6$
   (b) $(8 - 4) \times 2 = 8$
2. $5^2 = 25$; $81 - 16 = 65$
3. (a) 18 (b) 49 (c) 25 (d) 4
   (e) 10 (f) 48
4. 65.43
5. (a) 13 (b) 99
6. 63
7. 20

8. Upper and lower bounds
1. (a) 14.5 cm (b) 15.5 cm
2. (a) $8.5\,\text{cm} \leqslant w < 9.5\,\text{cm}$ (b) $5.5\,\text{kg} \leqslant m < 6.5\,\text{kg}$
   (c) $725\,\text{ml} \leqslant c < 775\,\text{ml}$ (d) $145\,\text{cm} \leqslant l < 155\,\text{cm}$
   (e) $1.95\,\text{litres} \leqslant c < 2.05\,\text{litres}$
3. Maximum capacity: 67.2 litres
   Minimum capacity: 60.8 litres
4. (a) 268.25 m² (b) 62 metres

9. Powers
1. (a) $7^2 \times 7^4 = 7^{2+4} = 7^6$
   (b) $6^9 \div 6^4 = 6^{9-4} = 6^5$
   (c) $10^3 \times 10 = 10^4$
   (d) $11^5 \div 11 = 11^4$
   (e) $(5^4)^3 = 5^{4 \times 3} = 5^{12}$
   (f) $(10^6)^5 = 10^{6 \times 5} = 10^{30}$
   (g) $3^5 \times 3^4 \div 3 = 3^{5+4-1} = 3^8$
   (h) $5^6 \times 5 \div 5^5 = 5^{6+1-5} = 5^2$
2. 7^2
3. $\frac{1}{81}$
4. (a) $\frac{1}{49}$ (b) $\frac{1}{64}$ (c) −27 (d) 64
   (e) $\frac{9}{100}$ (f) 15 (g) 1 (h) 6
   (i) 10

10. Standard form
1. (a) $3.2 \times 1000 = 3200$ (b) 480 000
   (c) 6250 (d) 70 910
   (e) $5.8 \div 1000 = 0.0058$ (f) 0.0345
   (g) 0.2094
2. (a) 7×10^3 (b) 5.2×10^3 (c) 8.67×10^5
3. (a) 1.23×10^{-1} (b) 2.9×10^{-3} (c) 9×10^{-2}
4. (a) 2.5×10^1 (b) 3.6×10^{-1} (c) 4.5×10^{-3} (d) 3.86×10^2
   (e) 3.006×10^{-2} (f) 6.8×10^4
5. (a) 3×10^2 (b) 3.598×10^4 (c) 4.2×10^3
6. 1.36×10^5 km

11. Calculator buttons
1. A (vi) B (v) C (vii) D (i) E (iii) F (ii) G (iv)
2. (a) (i) 2401 (ii) $\frac{1}{243}$ (iii) 23 (iv) 4
   (b) (i) 40 980 000 (ii) 86.8175
3. 5.583 (3 d.p.)
4. (a) $\frac{17}{6}$ (b) $\frac{44}{9}$
5. (a) $5\frac{2}{3}$ (b) $4\frac{1}{5}$ (c) $3\frac{8}{9}$
6. (a) $1\frac{7}{15}$ (b) $2\frac{19}{30}$ (c) $5\frac{1}{3}$ (d) $12\frac{2}{15}$
7. 31 000 grains (2 s.f.)

12. Prime factors
1. (a) $80 = 2 \times 2 \times 2 \times 2 \times 5$
   (b) $150 = 2 \times 3 \times 5 \times 5$
2. (a) $245 = 5 \times 7 \times 7 = 5 \times 7^2$
   (b) $320 = 2 \times 2 \times 2 \times 2 \times 2 \times 2 \times 5 = 2^6 \times 5$
3. 45 and 72
4. (a) $168 = 2^3 \times 3 \times 7$
   (b) $84^2 = 2^4 \times 3^2 \times 7^2$

13. HCF and LCM
1. (a) $32 = 2 \times 2 \times 2 \times 2 \times 2$; $56 = 2 \times 2 \times 2 \times 7$
   (b) HCF = 8; LCM = 224
2. (a) 24 (b) 144
3. 48 of each: 4 packs of pencils; 6 packs of pens
4. 14 m

14. Fractions and percentages

1. (a) £320 (b) £2000
2. (a) £112.50 (b) 1470 m*l* (c) 2.4 metres
3. (a) £80 (b) £2519.92
4. (a) £399.50 (b) £165.60 (c) £6.18
5. $\frac{7}{15}$ of £2540 = £1185.33, which is more than 45.6% of £2450 = £1117.20
6. (a) Cement: 3 kg; sand: 13.125 kg; gravel: 8.875 kg
   (b) 35.5%
7. 57.5% of £5100, $\frac{14}{17}$ of £3500, $\frac{13}{19}$ of £4200, 72% of £3800

15. Equivalence

1. (a) 65% (b) 20%
   (c) 8% (d) 0.34
   (e) 2.5 (f) 105%
2. (a) $\frac{6}{25}$ (b) $\frac{7}{20}$
   (c) $\frac{3}{5}$ (d) $\frac{9}{100}$
   (e) $\frac{2}{25}$ (f) $1\frac{3}{100}$
   (g) $1\frac{3}{20}$
3. (a) $\frac{27}{50} = \frac{54}{100} = 54\% \equiv 0.54$
   (b) $\frac{18}{24} = \frac{75}{100} = 75\% \equiv 0.75$
   (c) $\frac{28}{40} = 70\% \equiv 0.7$
4. 20%
5. Paper A (80%) Paper B (79.375%)
6. 40%

16. Recurring decimals

1. (a) $4.\dot{3}$ (b) $2.18\dot{6}$
   (c) $1.\dot{2}\dot{3}$ (d) $5.4\dot{5}\dot{6}$
2. (a) $1.\dot{4}$ (b) $4.\dot{3}$ (c) $5.91\dot{6}$
3. (a) $0.5\dot{4}$ (b) $0.\dot{8}$ (c) $2.08\dot{3}$
4. (a) $0.\dot{1}$ (b) $0.8\dot{9}$ (c) $0.\dot{7}0\dot{1}$
5. $\frac{7}{9} = 0.\dot{7}$; $\frac{5}{7} = 0.\dot{7}1428\dot{5}$; $\frac{2}{3} = 0.\dot{6}$; $\frac{7}{12} = 0.58\dot{3}$; $\frac{7}{8} = 0.875$; $\frac{8}{11} = 0.\dot{7}\dot{2}$
6. (a) Proof using division that $\frac{3}{7} = 0.\dot{4}2857\dot{1}$
   (b) Proof using division that $\frac{5}{12} = 0.41\dot{6}$
7. (a) $\frac{2}{9}$ (b) $\frac{3}{11}$ (c) $\frac{152}{333}$

17. Add and subtract fractions

1. (a) $\frac{1}{4} + \frac{3}{5} = \frac{5}{20} + \frac{12}{20} = \frac{17}{20}$
   (b) $\frac{7}{12} - \frac{1}{3} = \frac{7}{12} - \frac{4}{12} = \frac{3}{12} = \frac{1}{4}$
   (c) $\frac{4}{5} - \frac{2}{3} = \frac{12}{15} - \frac{10}{15} = \frac{2}{15}$
2. (a) $4\frac{1}{5} + 3\frac{3}{4} = (4+3) + \left(\frac{1}{5} + \frac{3}{4}\right) = 7 + \left(\frac{4}{20} + \frac{15}{20}\right) = 7\frac{19}{20}$
   (b) $4\frac{5}{6} - 2\frac{2}{3} = (4-2) + \left(\frac{5}{6} - \frac{2}{3}\right) = 2 + \left(\frac{5}{6} - \frac{4}{6}\right) = 2\frac{1}{6}$
   (c) $3\frac{5}{9} - 1\frac{1}{6} = (3-1) + \left(\frac{5}{9} - \frac{1}{6}\right) = 2 + \left(\frac{10}{18} - \frac{3}{18}\right) = 2\frac{7}{18}$
3. (a) $4\frac{1}{3} - 2\frac{5}{6} = (4-2) + \left(\frac{1}{3} - \frac{5}{6}\right)$
   $= 2 + \left(\frac{4}{12} - \frac{10}{12}\right) = 2 - \frac{1}{2} = 1\frac{1}{2}$
   (b) $2\frac{39}{40}$
4. $1\frac{17}{24}$ blocks
5. $\frac{8}{15}$ km

18. Multiply and divide fractions

1. (a) $2\frac{2}{5}$ (b) $\frac{8}{33}$ (c) $\frac{1}{3}$
2. (a) $2\frac{1}{2}$ (b) $3\frac{1}{2}$ (c) $7\frac{1}{2}$
3. (a) $\frac{2}{3}$ (b) 6 (c) $\frac{3}{4}$
4. (a) $\frac{21}{32}$ (b) $\frac{1}{8}$ (c) $\frac{2}{15}$ (d) $\frac{2}{3}$
   (e) $5\frac{1}{7}$ (f) $1\frac{4}{5}$
5. 6 lengths

19. Surds

1. $\sqrt{10}$ $\sqrt{2}$ $\sqrt{7}$
2. (a) $3\sqrt{3}$ (b) $6\sqrt{5}$ (c) $\frac{\sqrt{-7}}{8}$
3. (a) $3\sqrt{7}$ (b) $5\sqrt{2}$ (c) $6\sqrt{3}$
4. $2\sqrt{5}$
5. $7\sqrt{2}$

20. Number problem-solving

1. £52.30
2. (a) Browns £672.30   Greens £830   Blacks £987.70
   (b) 40%
3. (a) $M = 6\,350\,400 = 6.3504 \times 10^6$
       $N = 60\,368\,000 = 6.0368 \times 10^7$
   (b) HCF $= 2^6 \times 5^2 \times 7^2 = 78\,400 = 7.84 \times 10^4$
   (c) LCM $= 4.889\,808 \times 10^9$
4. (a) (i) 106.4475 cm² (ii) 108.5575 cm²
   (b) (i) 106 cm² (ii) 109 cm²
   (c) 42.4 − 42 = 0.4 cm

ALGEBRA

21. Indices

1. (a) t^7 (b) q^4 (c) g^{12} (d) a^4
   (e) $b^1 = b$ (f) $\frac{y^5}{y^6} = \frac{1}{y}$
2. (a) $8w^7$ (b) $-15p^4$ (c) $3h^2$
   (d) $\frac{-30s^6}{10s} = -3s^{6-1} = -3s^5$
3. (a) r^6 (b) $\frac{1}{k^6}$ (c) $t^{\frac{2}{3}}$ (d) $-12y^8$
   (e) -8 (f) $8k^8$
4. (a) $y + 3 = 7$ so $y = 4$ (b) $9 - y = 1$ so $y = 8$
   (c) $y \times 4 = 8$ so $y = 2$ (d) $-3 \times y = -9$ so $y = 3$
   (e) $y = 5$ (f) $y = 16$
   (g) $y = 27$

22. Simplifying expressions

1. (a) $2x + 3y$ (b) $10r + 3s$ (c) $-2p - 2q$
   (d) $-5t + 4u$ (e) $-6e - 3f + 4$ (f) $a - 2a^2$
2. (a) $12ab$ (b) $-15gh$ (c) $24y^2$
3. (a) 8 (b) $5g^2$ (c) $4b^2$
4. (a) $24abc$ (b) $-60k^2m$ (c) $6r^{-2}$
   (d) $14pq$ (e) $-9y^3$ (f) $7ab^{-1}$
5. $18x - 2y + 2$

23. Expanding brackets

1. (a) $20t - 10$ (b) $12f^2 - 20f$
   (c) $-12m^2 + 8mn$ (d) $-3a^3 - 4a^2b$
   (e) $6ab^3c^2 - 10a^2b^2c^2 + 14a^2b^5c$
2. (a) $14r^2q - 35r^3$ (b) $-20a^2b^3 + 15b^4$
   (c) $-12p^2q^3 + 8p^5q$
3. (a) $16xy - 15x^2 + 8y^2$ (b) $6ab + 12a^2 + 21b^2$
4. (a) $35a^2b^2 - 12a^3b + 9ab^3$ (b) $13c^2d - 5cd^2$
5. (a) LHS $= 6x^2 - 15xy =$ RHS
6. $10x^3y + 6x^2y^2$

24. Expanding double brackets

1. (a) $(x + 4)(x - 3) = x^2 - 3x + 4x - 12 = x^2 + x - 12$
   (b) $(x - 5)(x - 2) = x^2 - 2x - 5x + 10 = x^2 - 7x + 10$
2. (a) $(x + 3)(x + 6) = x^2 + 6x + 3x + 18 = x^2 + 9x + 18$
   (b) $(x - 5)(x + 4) = x^2 + 4x - 5x - 20 = x^2 - x - 20$
3. (a) $x^2 + 13x + 42$ (b) $x^2 - 5x - 36$
   (c) $x^2 - 10x + 16$ (d) $x^2 - 9$
   (e) $x^2 - 12x + 36$
4. (a) $6x^2 + 14x - 40$ (b) $16x^2 - 9$
   (c) $25x^2 + 60x + 36$
5. (a) RHS $= x^2 + 2bx + b^2 \neq$ LHS
6. $10x^2 + 29x - 21$

25. Factorising

1 (a) $8(3a - 2b)$ (b) $10(3y - 2)$ (c) $bc(3a - 7d)$

2 (a) $q^3(3q^2 + 8)$ (b) $e^6(2e + 1)$ (c) $d^2(6 - 7d^2)$

3 (a) $4b(3a - 2)$ (b) $10p(3pq + 2r)$ (c) $5pr(7q - 5s)$

4 (a) $5p(3pq + 4r)$ (b) $6p^2(3p^2 - 2)$ (c) $9x^4(3x + 4)$

5 (a) $4a(3b - a) = 12ab - 4a^2$

    (b) $15g^2 - 35gh = 5g(3g - 7h)$

6 (a) $(x + 7)(x - 2)$ (b) $(x + 3)(x + 8)$ (c) $(x + 6)^2$

7 $p = 3, q = 2$

26. More complex factorising

1 A (v)   B (i)   C (iv)   D (ii)   E (iii)

2 (a) $(x + 6)(x - 6)$ (b) $(x + 8)(x - 8)$

    (c) $(x + 12)(x - 12)$ (d) $(2x + 4)(2x - 4)$

    (e) $(5x + 7)(5x - 7)$ (f) $(9x + 10)(9x - 10)$

3 (a) 360   (b) 5200

    (c) 2400

4 (a) $(2x + 5)(x - 3)$ (b) $(3x + 7)(x - 2)$

    (c) $(5x + 2)(x + 3)$

5 LHS $= \dfrac{(3x + 4)(x + 3)}{3x + 4} = x + 3 = $ RHS

6 $40x$

27. Substitution

1 (a) 42   (b) 72   (c) $\frac{1}{3}$ (d) 135

    (e) 4   (f) 9

2 (a) 20   (b) 45   (c) 6   (d) 5

    (e) 126

3 Mary is wrong.

    When $x = 3$, $2x^3 = 2 \times 3^3 = 2 \times 27 = 54$; $216 = (2 \times 3)^3$

4 (a) 5   (b) 7   (c) 5   (d) 7

5 $mnp \ (= -70)$; $\dfrac{m^2 + n}{p} \ (= 9.4)$; $m + 2n + 3p \ (= 18)$;

    $(2m + n)(n + p) \ (= 36)$

28. The nth term

1 (a) $5 \times 4 - 1 = 19$

    (b) $3 \times 10 + 4 = 34$

    (c) $n = 1: 4 \times 1 + 1 = 5$

         $n = 2: 4 \times 2 + 1 = 9$

         $n = 3: 4 \times 3 + 1 = 13$

    (d) No. All terms are 1 more than a multiple of 5, whereas 45 is a multiple of 5.

2 (a) 11   (b) 8, 18, 28   (c) 8, 6, 4, 2, 0

    (d) Yes. All terms are 1 less than multiple of 5. $49 = 50 - 1$.

3 (a) $2n + 1$

    (b) $-3n + 19$ (c) $\dfrac{n}{2n + 1}$ (d) $\dfrac{2n - 1}{3n + 1}$

4 (a) (iii)   (b) (v)   (c) (ii)   (d) (i)   (e) (iv)

29. Non-linear sequences

1 Arithmetic: C, D; Geometric: A, E; Quadratic: B, F

2 No, 110 is not a square number. It is between 10^2 (100) and 11^2 (121).

3 (a) 1, 10, 25, 46, 73   (b) 10.5, 12, 14.5, 18, 22.5

    (c) $-12, -7, 0, 9, 20$

4 (a) $n^2 - 1$ (b) $2n^2$

5 (a) $\dfrac{n^2}{10}$ (b) $n^2 - 2$

    (c) $n^2 + 4$ (d) $2n^2 + 2$

6 $n^2 - 9$

30. Solving simple equations

1 (a) $x = 8$ (b) $y = 24$

2 (a) $z = 5$ (b) $x = 3$ (c) $q = 9$ (d) $x = 4$

3 6

4 (a) $x = 6$ (b) $y = 1$

5 (a) $a = 3$ (b) $y = 7$ (c) $x = 2$

6 6

7 $n = 7$

31. Solving complex equations

1 (a) $x = 7$ (b) $x = 8$

    (c) $x = 18$

2 $x = 2\frac{1}{7}$

3 (a) $x = 4$ (b) $x = -4\frac{2}{5}$

4 (a) $x = -4$ or $x = 2$ (b) $x = 3$ or $x = 5$

5 (a) $x = -5$ or $x = -4$ (b) $x = 6$

    (c) $x = 9$ or $x = -9$

6 $y = 10$

32. Writing and solving equations

1 (a) 9 cm   (b) 4 cm

2 Width 15 cm, length 9 cm

3 A 65°, B 70°, C 45°

4 40 cm

5 $x = 20°$, so $5x = 100°$, $3x - 40° = 20°$, $2x + 20° = 60°$

6 72 cm

33. Inequalities

1 (a) $-3 < x \leqslant 1$ (b) $-4 \leqslant x < 0$ (c) $x < 1$

2 (a) (i)

      (ii)

      (iii)

    (b) (i) $-4, -3, -2, -1, 0, 1$

        (ii) $-2, -1, 0, 1$

        (iii) $\ldots -1, 0, 1, 2, 3$

3 (a) $5x - 9 > 21$

       $5x > 21 + 9$

       $x > 30$

       $x > 6$

    (b) $6 - 3x \leqslant 18$

       $-3x \leqslant 12$

       $-x \leqslant 4$

       $x \geqslant -4$

4 (a) $x \leqslant 9$

    (b) $x \geqslant -9$

    (c) $x > -6$

5 $5x - 3 > 12: x > 3$

    $3x - 7 \leqslant 14: x \leqslant 7$

    so $x = 4, 5, 6, 7$

34. Inequalities on graphs

1

2

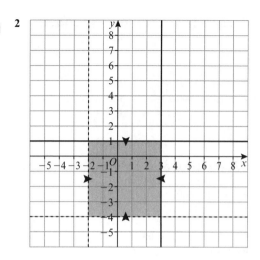

35. Simultaneous equations

1 (a) $x = 10$ $y = 3$ (b) $x = 8$ $y = 40$
2 (a) $x = 5$ $y = -2$ (b) $x = 3$ $y = 4$
3 1 apple costs 15p; 1 banana costs 25p.
4 1 large bench seats 8 pupils; 1 small bench seats 5 pupils.

36. Expression, equation, identity or formula?

1 A (iii)   B (iv)   C (ii)   D (i)
2 (a) formula   (b) equation
   (c) identity   (d) expression
   (e) expression   (f) equation
   (g) formula   (h) identity
3 (a) (i)   LHS: $(2 + 3)^2 = 5^2 = 25$
          RHS: $2^2 + (2 \times 2 \times 3) + 3^2 = 4 + 12 + 9 = 25 = $ LHS
      (ii) LHS: $(5 + 4)^2 = 9^2 = 81$
          RHS: $5^2 + (2 \times 5 \times 4) + 4^2 = 25 + 40 + 16 = 81 = $ LHS
      (iii) LHS: $(-6 + -1)^2 = (-7)^2 = 49$
          RHS: $(-6)^2 + (2 \times -6 \times -1) + (-1)^2 = 36 + 12 + 1$
          $= 49 = $ LHS
4 Either algebraic proof or three numerical solutions to show LHS = RHS
5 Either algebraic proof or three numerical solutions to show LHS $\neq$ RHS

37. Rearranging formulae

1 (a) 120   (b) 8
2 (a) $a = \dfrac{b - 8}{5}$ (b) $x = \sqrt{y}$ (c) $t = \sqrt{\dfrac{b}{3}}$
3 (a) $x = \dfrac{20 - 2y}{3}$ (b) $q = \dfrac{r(3p - 5)}{2}$ (c) $b = 25a^2 - c$
4 (a) $x = \dfrac{4}{a + b}$ (b) $x = \dfrac{4q - 7p}{5p - 3q}$
5 (a) £8000   (b) £28 000
6 (a) $r = \sqrt{\dfrac{V}{\pi h}}$ (b) 6 cm

38. Using formulae

1 (a) $A = 439.82\,\text{cm}^2$ (2 d.p.)
   (b) $h = 12.01\,\text{cm}$ (2 d.p.)
2 (a) $c = 5\,\text{cm}$ (b) $a = 9\,\text{cm}$
3 (a) $a = 144$ (b) $b = 1.\dot{6}$ (c) $c = 1.58$ (2 d.p.)
4 (a) $V = 2211.68\,\text{cm}^3$ (2 d.p.)
   (b) $h = 4.14\,\text{cm}$ (2 d.p.)
   (c) 4.50 cm (2 d.p.)

39. Writing formulae

1 (a) $C = 24h + 2$ (b) £86   (c) 2 hours
2 (a) $C = 9L + 7S$ (b) £124   (c) 9 small houses
3 (a) $M = 120S + 150L$ (b) 1.71 kg   (c) 4 small boxes
4 (a) $T = 2c + 3b + 2.5p$ (b) £90   (c) 5 of each

40. Midpoint and gradient

1 (a) (i) (1, 3)   (ii) (5, 1)   (b) (3, 2)
2 (5, 9)
3 (a) (2, 6)   (b) (5, −4)
4 (a) 2   (b) $-\frac{1}{4}$
5 (a) $\frac{1}{2}$ (b) $-\frac{1}{3}$

41. $y = mx + c$

1 (a) 2   (b) −1   (c) $y = 2x - 1$
2 $y = -3x + 1$
3 (a)

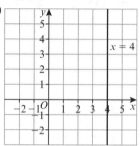

   (b)

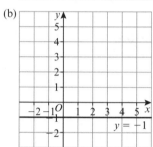

4 (a) B (b) A (c) D (d) C

42. Straight-line graphs

1 (a)

x	0	1	2	3	4
y	1	4	7	10	13

   (b)

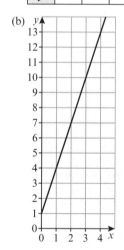

2

x	0	1	2	3	4	5	6
y	6	5	4	3	2	1	0

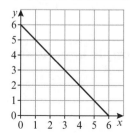

3

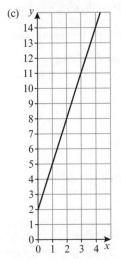

43. Parallel and perpendicular

1   *A* and *D*
2   Any equation of the form $y = -5x + c$
3   (a) Yes
    (b) Gradient of line between
    $$A \text{ and } B = \frac{\text{distance up}}{\text{distance across}} = \frac{9-5}{4-2} = \frac{4}{2} = 2$$
    The gradient of the line $y = 2x + 5$ is 2
    The gradients of the lines are the same so the lines are parallel.
4   (a) $-\frac{1}{4}$ (b) 3
5   The gradient of *L* is 7
    The gradient of *P* is 7
    The equation of *P* is $y = 7x - 3$
6   $y = -2x + 6$

44. Formulae from graphs and tables

1   (a) $P = 3d + 2$

(b)
Distance, *d* (km)	0	1	2	3	4
Charge, *P* (£)	2	5	8	11	14

(c)

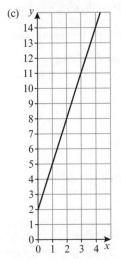

(d) approx. 2.7 km
2   (a) $P = 40h + 20$
    (b) 3 hours

45. Quadratic graphs

1   (a)
x	−3	−2	−1	0	1	2
y	3	0	−1	0	3	8

(b)

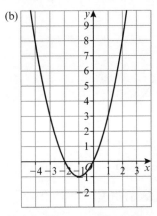

(c) (−1, −1)   (d) minimum   (e) $x = -1$

2   (a)
x	−2	−1	0	1	2	3	4
y	5	0	−3	−4	−3	0	5

(b)

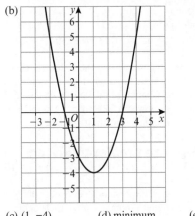

(c) (1, −4)   (d) minimum   (e) $x = 1$

46. Other non-linear graphs

1   (a)
x	−2	−1	0	1	2
y	−6	1	2	3	10

(b)

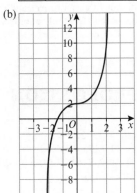

2 (a)

x	0.5	1	1.5	2	2.5	3	3.5	4
y	8	4	2.7	2	1.6	1.3	1.1	1

(b)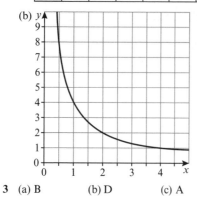

3 (a) B   (b) D   (c) A   (d) C

47. Real-life graphs
1 (a) It converts between gallons and litres.
  (b) 0.1 gallons
  (c) 18 litres
  (d) 5.5 gallons
  (e) 2.4 gallons is slightly less than 11 litres, so 12 litres is more.
2 (a) 2009
  (b) 2013−2015
  (c) (i) £1 ≈ €1.25   (ii) £1 ≈ €1.19
  (d) €0.09
  (e) The graph shows that the exchange rate fluctuates from year to year. Although there is an overall increasing trend, it cannot be predicted with confidence that the rate was lower in 2008 than it was in 2009 or that it will be higher in 2016 than it was in 2015.

48. Algebra problem-solving
1 (a) $(3x + 20) + (2x − 40) + (4x − 20) + x = 10x − 40 = 360$
  (b) $x = 40°$
  (c) $x = 40°$, $3x + 20 = 140°$, $2x − 40 = 40°$, $4x − 20 = 140°$
  (d) It could be a rhombus or a parallelogram because opposite angles are equal.
2 (a) 16 °C
  (b) January, February, December
  (c) The highest point of the graph line shows the hottest month, which is July.
  (d) The graph shows that the temperature increases from February until July (it gets warmer), and then it decreases (cools down) from July until December. It doesn't change from December to February.
  (e) 50 °F
3 Coffee: £1.50; Tea: £1.25

RATIO & PROPORTION

49. Ratio
1 (a) cotton : polyester = 75 : 25 = 3 : 1
  (b) sugar : butter = 125 : 175 = 5 : 7
2 7 + 2 = 9; 450 ÷ 9 = £50; 7 × 50 = £350; 2 × 50 = £100
  Check: £350 + £100 = £450
3 10 boys, 12 girls
4 80 grams
5 (a) 1 : 10   (b) 1 : 1.8   (c) 1 : 12   (d) 1 : 1.6
6 (a) £35   (b) £84

50. Direct proportion
1 (a) £136 ÷ 8 = £17; 15 × £17 = £255
  (b) £12.50
2 (a) 10 for £48   (b) 8 for £120
3 (a) £14.40   (b) £2.16
4 (a) £649.60   (b) $246.31   (c) £280
5 (a) 12.76 pounds   (b) 6.5 kg   (c) 57 kg
6 C

51. Inverse proportion
1 C
2 (a) 3 electricians × 2 days = 6 days' work
     6 days' work ÷ 6 electricians = 1 day
  (b) 6 days ÷ 2 electricians = 3 days
3 (a) 6 hours
  (b) 2 painters
4 Pairs A and D, and B and C, are in inverse proportion.

	x	y	xy
A	2.4	10	2.4 × 10 = 24
B	2.5	9.24	2.5 × 9.24 = 23.1
C	2.2	10.5	2.2 × 10.5 = 23.1
D	3.2	7.5	3.2 × 7.5 = 24

5 (a)

Runners	Amount
4	£240 ÷ 4 = £60
5	£240 ÷ 5 = £48
6	£240 ÷ 6 = £40
8	£240 ÷ 8 = £30
10	£240 ÷ 10 = £24

  (b) This example shows inverse proportion because as the number of runners increases, the amount each needs to raise decreases, and their product is constant.

52. Maps and scales
1 (a) 8 × 12 = 96 m   (b) 78 ÷ 12 = 6.5 cm
2 (a) 1.2 km   (b) 5 cm
3 4.96 cm
4 (a) 90 m
  (b) Robert is correct. The distance from the entrance to the playground is 6 cm on the map, which represents 180 m in real life, so is less than 200 m.
  (c) A point marked exactly 4 cm from the lake.

53. Speed, distance, time
1 Speed = distance ÷ time = 140 ÷ 2 = 70 km/h
2 20 km/h
3 2 hours and 30 minutes = 2.5 hours
  Distance = speed × time = 90 × 2.5 = 225 miles
4 15 km
5 3 hours and 30 minutes
6 6 km

54. Distance−time graphs
1 (a) 125 miles   (b) 250 miles
  (c) $2\frac{3}{4}$ hours   (d) 1.30 pm
  (e) speed = distance ÷ time = 50 ÷ 1 = 50 mph
  (f) speed = 125 ÷ 2 = 62.5 mph
  (g) They travelled fastest during the return journey, when their speed was 62.5 mph (compared with 50 mph and 60 mph for the other sections). This is the steepest line on the graph.
2 (a) 4 km   (b) 3 km/h   (c) 2 hours
  (d)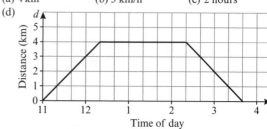

  (e) 3.40 pm

55. Density

1. (a) $M = D \times V$; g or kg
   (b) $D = M \div V$; g/cm^3 or kg/m^3
   (c) $V = M \div D$; cm^3 or m^3
2. 3140 kg/m^3
3. (a) 89 cm^3 (b) 110 grams
4. (a) 1.929 g/cm^3 (b) 7049 kg/m^3
5. (a) 457 grams
   (b) Olive oil will float on pure water, because the density of oil (0.913 g/cm^3) is less than the density of water (1 g/cm^3).

56. Graphs of rates of change

1. (a) D (i)   (b) B (iv)   (c) A (ii)   (d) C (iii)
2. (a)   (b)   (c)

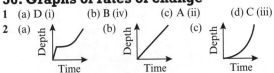

3. (a)

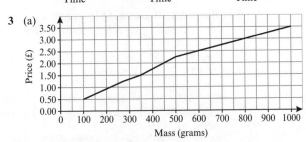

   (b) The graph shows that the price of grain is not proportional to its mass because it is not a straight line showing a constant rate of change.

57. Percentage change

1. (a) £765   (b) £975   (c) £2984.52   (d) £6615.96
   (e) €4104   (f) £1050
2. £2898
3. 42 141
4. Company B offers better value (€900 compared with €880.40).
5. $109.69
6. (a) 16%   (b) 19%

58. Reverse percentages

1. (a) £480   (b) £120
2. (a) $12   (b) £60   (c) £6000   (d) £540
3. 240
4. £3600
5. £3500

59. Compound interest

1. (a)

Year	Starting balance (£)	Interest (£)	New balance (£)
1	2600	2600 × 0.02 = 52	2600 + 52 = 2652
2	2652	2652 × 0.02 = 53.04	2652 + 53.04 = 2705.04
3	2705.04	2705.04 × 0.02 = 54.10	2705.04 + 54.10 = 2759.14
4	2759.14	2759.14 × 0.02 = 55.18	2759.14 + 55.18 = 2814.32

   (b) £2814.32   (c) £214.32
   (d) More interest was earned in years 3 and 4 because the starting balance for these years was higher than for years 1 and 2.
2. (a) Final balance: $3200 \times (1.03)^4 = £3601.63$
      Interest: $3601.63 - 3200 = £401.63$
   (b) Final balance: $5750 \times (1.035)^5 = £6829.20$
      Interest: $6829.20 - 5750 = £1079.20$
3. Annie (£292.10) earns more interest than Hugh (£254.37).
4. £11 851
5. 6 years; $280 \times 0.825^5 = £107.01$; $280 \times 0.825^6 = £88.28$

60. Proportion problem-solving

1. Box A: 0.598p per gram; Box B: 0.6p per gram; Box C: 0.63p per gram
   Box A is the best value because it costs the least per gram.
2. (a) Simple interest is higher (£240 compared with £232.65).
   (b) Compound interest is higher (£602 compared with £600).
3. 165 km/h (45.8$\dot{3}$ m/s) is faster than 45 m/s (162 km/h).
4. The wood has the greater density (3.33 g/cm^3 = 3330 kg/m^3 compared with 2480 kg/m^3 = 2.48 g/cm^3).

GEOMETRY & MEASURES

61. Perimeter and area

1. (a) Area of a triangle $= \frac{1}{2} \times$ base $\times$ height
      $= \frac{1}{2} \times 35 \times 12 = 210$ cm^2
   (b) Perimeter $= 12 + 37 + 35 = 84$ cm
2. (a) $x + 7 + x + 7 = 22$
      $2x + 14 = 22$
      $2x = 8$
      $x = 4$ mm
   (b) Area = 28 mm^2
3. (a) 51.2 m^2 (b) 36 cm^2
4. $h = 4$ cm

62. Compound shapes

1. Area of rectangle A = 3 × 5 = 15 cm^2
   Area of rectangle B = 4 × 6 = 24 cm^2
   Area of shape = 24 + 15 = 39 cm^2
2. 38 cm^2
3. (a) Area = 66 m^2
   (b) Perimeter = 38 m, so kerb is 34 m
4. Area of card = 210 cm^2

63. Circles

1. Circumference $= \pi d$
      $= \pi \times 12 = 37.7$ cm (1 d.p.)
2. 188.5 cm (1 d.p.)
3. (a) 452.4 cm^2
   (b) 706.9 cm^2
4. 100π cm^2
5. (a) 6.4 cm
   (b) 3.2 cm
   (c) 31.8 cm^2

64. Sectors of circles

1. Area of a sector $= \frac{\theta}{360} \times \pi r^2$
      $= \frac{30}{360} \times \pi \times 5^2$
      $= \frac{1}{12} \times \pi \times 25$
      $= 6.54498... = 6.5$ cm^2 (1 d.p.)
2. 50.27 cm^2
3. Length of arc $= \frac{\theta}{360} \times 2\pi r$
      $= \frac{69}{360} \times \pi \times 2 \times 15$
      $= 15.7079... = 15.7$ cm (1 d.p.)
   Perimeter $= 15.7 + 15 + 15$
      $= 45.7$ cm (1 d.p.)
4. 36.85 m (2 d.p.)
5. Shape B has the greater area (78.54 cm^2 compared with 62.83 cm^2).

65. Circles problem-solving

1. (a) Area of square = 5 × 5 = 25 cm^2
      Area of quarter circle $= \frac{1}{4}(\pi \times r^2)$
         $= \frac{1}{4} \times \pi \times 5^2$
         $= 19.6349... = 19.6$ cm^2 (1 d.p.)
      Shaded area = area of square − area of quarter circle
         $= 25 - 19.6 = 5.4$ cm^2 (1 d.p.)

(b) Percentage shaded $= \dfrac{\text{shaded area}}{\text{area of square}} \times 100$

$\qquad\qquad\qquad = 21.46 = 21\%$ (to nearest 1 per cent)

(c) Perimeter $= 17.9$ cm (1 d.p.)

2   Area of large sector $= 294.5243...$ cm^2
    Area of small sector $= 130.8996...$ cm^2
    Shaded area $= 163.6246... = 164$ cm^2 (3 s.f.)

3   Perimeter $= 40\pi$ cm

66. Plans and elevations

1

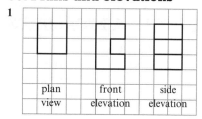

plan view   front elevation   side elevation

2

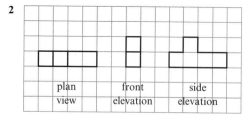

plan view   front elevation   side elevation

3

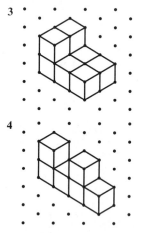

4

67. Surface area

1   126 cm^2

2   Area of left triangular face $= \frac{1}{2} \times 9 \times 12 = 54$ cm^2
    Area of right triangular face $= \frac{1}{2} \times 9 \times 12 = 54$ cm^2
    Area of bottom face $= 12 \times 10 = 120$ cm^2
    Area of back face $= 9 \times 10 = 90$ cm^2
    Area of slanted face $= 15 \times 10 = 150$ cm^2
    Total surface area $= 54 + 54 + 120 + 90 + 150 = 468$ cm^2

3   158 cm^2

68. Volume

1   (a) Volume of prism $=$ area of cross-section $\times$ length
                      $= 24 \times 9 = 216$ cm^3
    (b) Volume $= 12 \times 6 = 72$ m^3

2   90 mm^3

3   36 cm^3

4   310 cm^3

69. Cylinders

1   (a) Volume $=$ area of cross-section $\times$ height
       $= \pi \times 6^2 \times 9 = 1017.8760... = 1017.9$ cm^3 (1 d.p.)
    (b) Surface area $= 2\pi rh + 2\pi r^2$
                  $= 2 \times \pi \times 6 \times 9 + 2 \times \pi \times 6^2$
                  $= 339.2920... + 226.1946...$
                  $= 565.4866... = 565.5$ cm^2 (1 d.p.)

2   (a) 62.8 m^3 (3 s.f.)
    (b) 132 m^2 (3 s.f.)

3   439.8 cm^3 (1 d.p.)

70. Angle facts

1   Angle $DCE = 180 - 138 = 42°$
    Reason: angles on a straight line add up to 180°
    Angle $DEC = 180 - 74 = 106°$
    Reason: angles on a straight line add up to 180°
    Angle $x = 180 - (42 + 106) = 32°$
    Reason: angles in a triangle add up to 180°

2   (a) $a = 112°$; alternate angles are equal
    (b) $b = 54°$; corresponding angles are equal
    (c) $c = 57°$; co-interior angles add up to 180°

3   Largest angle is 132°

4   (a) $a = 83°$; corresponding angles are equal and angles in a triangle add up to 180°
    (b) $b = 120°$; angles on a straight line add up to 180° and corresponding angles are equal, or vertically opposite angles are equal and co-interior angles add up to 180°.

71. Angles in parallelograms

1   Angle $TSV = 60°$ (opposite angles of a parallelogram are equal)
    Angle $RST = 120°$ (angles on a straight line add up to 180°)

2   Angle $ABC = 130°$ (opposite angles of a parallelogram are equal)
    Angle $BAE = 50°$ (co-interior angles add up to 180°)
    Angle $AEB = 50°$ (base angles of an isosceles triangle are equal)
    Angle $ABE = 80°$ (angles in a triangle add up to 180°)
    $x = 130 - 80 = 50°$

3   $x = 64°$ (alternate angles are equal)
    $y = 180 - 52 = 128°$ (co-interior angles add up to 180°)

4   (a) $x = 10°$ so angle $BCD = 60°$ (opposite angles of a parallelogram are equal)
    (b) Angle $ABC = 120°$ (co-interior angles are equal)

72. Angles in polygons

1   Sum of interior angles $= (n - 2) \times 180$
                          $= (8 - 2) \times 180 = 6 \times 180 = 1080°$

2   (a) 6 sides   (b) hexagon

3   (a) Exterior angles of a polygon add up to 360°
       Exterior angle of a regular 12-sided polygon $= \dfrac{360}{12} = 30°$
    (b) Interior angle + exterior angle $= 180°$
       Interior angle $= 180 - 30 = 150°$

4   (a) 60°   (b) 120°

5   160°

73. Angles problem-solving

1   Sum of interior angles $= (n - 2) \times 180$
                          $= (6 - 2) \times 180$
                          $= 4 \times 180 = 720°$
    $a + 120 + 85 + 102 + 145 + 125 = 720$
    $a = 720 - 577 = 143°$

2   $x = 36°$

3   $y = 51.4°$ (1 d.p.)

74. Pythagoras' theorem

1   $c^2 = a^2 + b^2$
    $x^2 = 5^2 + 6^2$
    $x^2 = 61$
     $x = \sqrt{61}$
      $= 7.8102...$
      $x = 7.8$ cm (1 d.p.)

2   $y = 7.6$ cm

3   $c^2 = a^2 + b^2$
    $h^2 = 10^2 - 4^2$
    $h^2 = 84$
     $h = \sqrt{84}$
      $= 9.1651...$
     $h = 9.2$ m (1 d.p.)

4   $p = 5.7$ cm

5   Height $= 8.9$ cm

75. Trigonometry 1

1 (a) (b) (c)

2 $\tan x = \dfrac{\text{opposite}}{\text{adjacent}}$

$= \dfrac{8}{6}$

$x = \tan^{-1}\left(\dfrac{8}{6}\right)$

$= 53.1201...$

$= 53.1°$ (1 d.p.)

3 $y = 36.9°$

4 $z = 44.4°$

76. Trigonometry 2

1 $\cos \theta = \dfrac{\text{adjacent}}{\text{hypotenuse}}$

$\cos 42° = \dfrac{x}{22}$

$x = 22 \times \cos 42°$

$= 16.3491... = 16.3\,\text{cm}$ (1 d.p.)

2 $y = 6.5\,\text{m}$ (1 d.p.)

3 $p = 22.0\,\text{cm}$ (3 s.f.)

4 $b = 26.4\,\text{mm}$ (1 d.p.)

77. Problem-solving with triangles

1 (a) $(AC)^2 = (AB)^2 + (BC)^2$

$= 10\,000 + 6400$

$AC = \sqrt{16\,400} = 128\,\text{km}$

Total distance $= 100 + 80 + 128 = 308\,\text{km}$

(b) $\tan \theta = \dfrac{\text{opposite}}{\text{adjacent}} = \dfrac{100}{80}$

$\theta = \tan^{-1}\left(\dfrac{100}{80}\right) = 51.34°$

2 $\theta = 67°$

3 (a) $BC = 6.39\,\text{m}$ (2 d.p.)

(b) Area $= 26\,\text{m}^2$

78. Constructions 1

1 Accurate construction of triangle

2 Accurate construction of perpendicular bisector

79. Constructions 2

1 Accurate construction of angle bisector

2 Accurate constructions of perpendicular bisector and then angle bisector to give 45° angle

3 Accurate construction of 30° angle

80. Loci

1 (a)

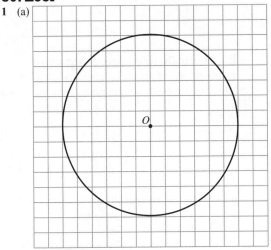

(b)

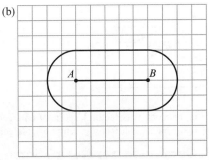

2

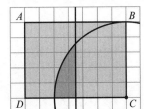

3

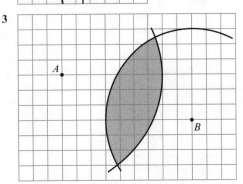

81. Transformations

1

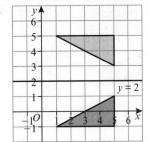

2 (a) Rotation 180° about (0, 1)

(b) Rotation 90° anticlockwise about (0,0)

3 (a) Translation by the vector $\begin{pmatrix} 3 \\ 1 \end{pmatrix}$

(b) Translation by the vector $\begin{pmatrix} -5 \\ 2 \end{pmatrix}$

(c) Translation by the vector $\begin{pmatrix} 5 \\ -2 \end{pmatrix}$

(d) They are opposites; signs change, with positive becoming negative and vice versa.

82. Enlargement

1

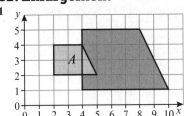

2

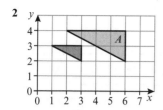

3 Enlargement, scale factor 3, centre of enlargement (−1, 2)

4 Enlargement, scale factor $\frac{1}{3}$, centre of enlargement (2, 3)

83. Combined transformations

1 (a) and (b)

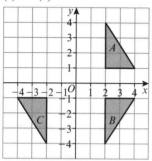

(c) Rotation 180° about centre (0, 0)

2 (a) and (b)

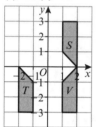

(c) Reflection in the x-axis

3 (a) and (b)

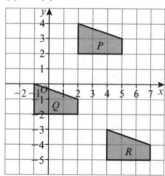

(c) Translation by the vector $\begin{pmatrix} 2 \\ -7 \end{pmatrix}$

(d) Translation by the vector $\begin{pmatrix} -2 \\ 7 \end{pmatrix}$

(e) The signs for the numbers in the vectors have changed.

84. Congruent shapes

1 Triangle GHI is congruent to triangle ABC because two angles are the same and the side between them is the same.

2 Angle SXT = angle VXU because vertically opposite angles are equal.
Angle VUS = angle TSU because alternate angles are equal.
Angle TVU = angle STV because alternate angles are equal.
$ST = VU$ (given)
So triangle STX is congruent to triangle VUX (AAS)

3 Appropriate demonstration of congruence, e.g.
Side AC is shared.
$AD = BC$ (opposite sides of rectangle are equal)
$AB = CD$ (opposite sides of rectangle are equal)
So triangles ABC and CDA are congruent (SSS)

Or:
Side AC is shared.
Angle ADC = angle ABC (right angle)
AB and CD are parallel (opposite sides of rectangle)
Angle DAC = angle ACB (alternate angles are equal)
Angle ACD = angle BAC (alternate angles are equal)
So triangles ABC and CDA are congruent (ASA)

85. Similar triangles

1 The triangles are similar because (i) the corresponding sides are in the same ratio, or (ii) each side is multiplied by the same scale factor, 2

2 (a) Scale factor (SF) = $\frac{15}{6}$ = 2.5
$p = 8 \times$ SF = $8 \times 2.5 = 20\,cm$
(b) SF = $\frac{6}{15}$ = 0.4
$q = 10 \times$ SF = $10 \times 0.4 = 4\,cm$

3 $PT = 2.5\,cm$

PROBABILITY

86. Experimental probability

1 Estimate for number of 3s = $0.5 \times 200 = 100$

2 (a) P(orange) = $\frac{9}{30} = \frac{3}{10}$
(b) P(yellow) = $300 \times \frac{8}{30}$

3 (a) $\frac{12}{40} = \frac{3}{10}$
(b) 50

4 200

87. Probability diagrams

1 (a)

		Spinner				
		1	**2**	**3**	**4**	**5**
Coin	**H**	H1	H2	H3	H4	H5
	T	T1	T2	T3	T4	T5

(b) $\frac{2}{10} = \frac{1}{5}$

2 (a)

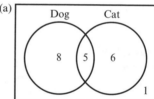

(b) $\frac{8}{20} = \frac{2}{5}$

3 (a)

	Cinema	Theatre	Total
Adults	10	12	22
Children	18	5	23
Total	28	17	45

(b) $\frac{28}{45}$

88. Probability tree diagrams

1 (a) P(does not win) = 1 − P(wins) = $1 - 0.7 = 0.3$

(b)

1st game	2nd game	Outcome	Probability
0.7 Wins	0.7 Wins	WW	$0.7 \times 0.7 = 0.49$
	0.3 Does not win	WD	$0.7 \times 0.3 = 0.21$
0.3 Does not win	0.7 Wins	DW	$0.3 \times 0.7 = 0.21$
	0.3 Does not win	DD	$0.3 \times 0.3 = 0.09$

(c) 0.09

(d) $0.7 \times 0.3 + 0.3 \times 0.7 = 0.21 + 0.21 = 0.42$

2 (a) $\frac{1}{5}$

(b)

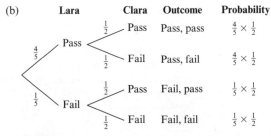

	Lara	Clara	Outcome	Probability

Pass $\frac{4}{5}$, Pass $\frac{1}{2}$ — Pass, pass — $\frac{4}{5} \times \frac{1}{2}$

Fail $\frac{1}{2}$ — Pass, fail — $\frac{4}{5} \times \frac{1}{2}$

Fail $\frac{1}{5}$, Pass $\frac{1}{2}$ — Fail, pass — $\frac{1}{5} \times \frac{1}{2}$

Fail $\frac{1}{2}$ — Fail, fail — $\frac{1}{5} \times \frac{1}{2}$

(c) $\frac{4}{10}$ or $\frac{2}{5}$

(d) $\frac{5}{10}$ or $\frac{1}{2}$

89. Mutually exclusive and independent events

1 (a) Mutually exclusive because you cannot spin a 3 and a 7 at the same time.

(b) Not mutually exclusive because 6 is both even and a multiple of 3.

(c) Mutually exclusive because you cannot get an even number which is also an odd number.

(d) Not mutually exclusive as both 2 and 1 are factors of 6 and 8.

2 (a) Not independent; having lent a green pen affects the probability of picking another green pen.

(b) Independent; spinning a 2 does not affect what happens when you flip the coin.

3 $\frac{2}{6}$ or $\frac{1}{3}$

4 0.64

5 $\frac{1}{216}$

STATISTICS

90. Averages and range

1 (a) The mode is 5.

(b) Mean = $\dfrac{4 + 5 + 12 + 1 + 5 + 3 + 4 + 10 + 5 + 1}{10} = \dfrac{50}{10} = 5$

(c) Median = $\dfrac{4 + 5}{2} = 4.5$

(d) Range = $12 - 1 = 11$

2 (a) Mode = 88; Median = 84; Mean = 77.1

(b) The median is the best average to use; the low score of 20 is not typical, and it affects the mean; the mode of 88 is Jenny's top score; so the median is the best average because it is not skewed by extreme results at either end.

3 4 and 6

91. Averages from tables

1 (a) Mode = 2 points

(b)

Number of points x	Frequency f	$x \times f$
0	1	$0 \times 1 = 0$
1	3	$1 \times 3 = 3$
2	8	$2 \times 8 = 16$
3	5	$3 \times 5 = 15$
4	3	$4 \times 3 = 12$

Mean = $\dfrac{\text{total number of points}}{\text{total frequency}} = \dfrac{46}{20} = 2.3$ points

2

Age, a (years)	Frequency f	Midpoint x	$f \times x$
$20 < a \leqslant 30$	5	25	$5 \times 25 = 125$
$30 < a \leqslant 40$	10	35	$10 \times 35 = 350$
$40 < a \leqslant 50$	4	45	$4 \times 45 = 180$
$50 < a \leqslant 60$	6	55	$6 \times 55 = 330$

Mean = $\dfrac{985}{25} = 39.4$ years

3 £83

92. Two-way tables

1 (a)

	Cat	Dog	Other	Total
Year 7	10	9	11	30
Year 8	13	12	5	30
Total	23	21	16	60

(b) 12 children

2 (a)

	Museum	Art gallery	Zoo	Total
Adults	9	10	12	31
Children	15	8	16	39
Total	24	18	28	70

(b) 16 children

3 (a)

	Hot drink	Cold drink	Total
Adults	12	8	20
Children	10	15	25
Total	22	23	45

(b) 10 children

4 7 girls

93. Analysing data

1 B

2 B and C

3 His friends may have the same interests and like the same football teams, so the sample would not be random.

4) (a) 70

(b) A, B and C

(c) For example:

Favourite film genre	Tally	Frequency
Drama		
Horror		
Science fiction		
Romance		

94. Interpreting charts

1 (a) 120° represents 6 students so 20° represents 1 student. Number of students who prefer texting = $160° \div 20° = 8$

(b) $360° \div 20° = 18$

2 (a) 10 matches

(b) 20 matches

3 (a) Range = 31

(b) Mode = 29

(c) Median = 17

95. Misleading graphs and charts

1 In 2014, the total sales were £100 000
In 2015, the total sales were £120 000
The sales have increased by £20 000, not £200 000
The graph is misleading because the scale on the vertical axis does not start at zero / does not increase in equal increments.

2 Pie charts show proportions of the total number – they do not show actual numbers.
The proportion of games won in March is approximately $\frac{1}{4}$.
The proportion won in April is approximately $\frac{1}{3}$.
You cannot tell from the pie charts how many games were won in March or April because you don't know how many games were played.

3 (a) The sales director is using graph B; the vertical scale on graph B has smaller increments so it looks like the number of customers is increasing more.

(b) Graph B is misleading because the scale on the vertical axis does not start at zero.

96. Scatter graphs

1 (a) As the temperature increases the number of ice creams sold increases.
 (b) Positive
 (c) Line of best fit drawn
 (d) 8 ice creams

2 (a) As the age of a car increases its value decreases.
 (b) Negative
 (c) A value between £3000 and £4000

97. Frequency polygons

1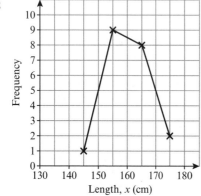
Ages of people in a choir

2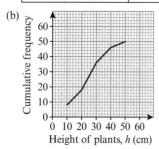

98. Cumulative frequency

1 (a) 12−13 students
 (b) 5.4−5.6 hours
 (c) About 7 − 4.2 = 2.8 hours

2 (a)

Height of plants, h (cm)	Frequency	Cumulative frequency
$0 < h \leqslant 10$	8	8
$10 < h \leqslant 20$	10	18
$20 < h \leqslant 30$	18	36
$30 < h \leqslant 40$	10	46
$40 < h \leqslant 50$	4	50

(b)

(c) About 23−24 cm
(d) About 31 − 15 = 16 cm

99. Box plots

1 (a) Soil B
 (b) 10 cm
 (c) Soil B was better than soil A because the median height for soil B (13 cm) is greater than the median for soil A (9 cm). The interquartile range for soil B (8 cm) is less than the interquartile range for soil A (10 cm) so the heights are less spread out for B.

2 (a) £60   (b) £42
 (c)

Money (£)

(d) Year 9 performed better. The median for Year 9 is £66 which is larger than the median for Year 8 (£60); the interquartile range for Year 9 is £32 which is smaller than the interquartile range for Year 8 (£42).

100. Writing a report

The estimated mean is 25.2 minutes.
The modal group is $10 < t \leqslant 20$ minutes.
The median class interval is $20 < t \leqslant 30$ minutes.
The estimated range = largest value − smallest value
= 60 − 0 = 60 minutes

Time spent shopping

An appropriate conclusion that is supported by the averages calculated states whether the statistics support the hypothesis and makes appropriate suggestions to improve the investigation. For example:
The estimated range of times spent shopping is 60 minutes but this is affected by an outlier of one person who took $50 < t \leqslant 60$ minutes to shop. If we ignore the outlier the estimated range is 50 minutes. The estimated mean and modal class are both less than 30 minutes, and the median class interval is $20 < t \leqslant 30$ minutes. Karen has **not** proved her hypothesis that people spend more than 30 minutes shopping. To improve her investigation, Karen could: ask more people; find out whether people spend longer shopping at weekends than on weekdays; see whether men spend more or less time shopping than women; see whether younger people spend more or less time shopping than older people.

Notes

Notes

Notes

Notes

Notes

Published by Pearson Education Limited, 80 Strand, London, WC2R 0RL

www.pearsonschoolsandfecolleges.co.uk

Text and illustrations © Pearson Education Limited 2016

Typeset by Tech-Set Ltd, Gateshead

Produced by Cambridge Publishing Management Ltd

Illustrated by Cambridge Publishing Management Ltd and Tech-Set Ltd, Gateshead

Cover illustration by Miriam Sturdee

The rights of Sharon Bolger and Bobbie Johns to be identified as authors of this work have been asserted by them in accordance with the Copyright, Designs and Patents Act 1988.

First published 2016

19 18 17 16

10 9 8 7 6 5 4 3 2 1

British Library Cataloguing in Publication Data

A catalogue record for this book is available from the British Library

ISBN 978 1 292 11150 6

Printed in Slovakia by Neografia